Homework Boo

Delivering the AQA Specification

GW00363018

NEW GCSE MATHS
AQA Modular

Matches the 2010 GCSE Specification

Brian Speed • Keith Gordon • Kevin Evans
Trevor Senior • Chris Pearce

CONTENTS

RECALL

UNIT 3: Geometry and Algebra

INTRODUCTION

Welcome to Collins New GCSE Maths for AQA Modular Higher Homework Book 2. This book follows the structure of the AQA Modular Higher Student Book. The first part of this book covers the Recall content you will have learnt in Unit 1 and Unit 2. You will also need some content covered in this section in your Unit 3 exam. The second part covers content specific to Unit 3.

Colour-coded grades

Know what target grade you are working at and track your progress with the colour-coded grade panels at the side of the page.

Use of calculators

Questions when you could use a calculator are marked with a 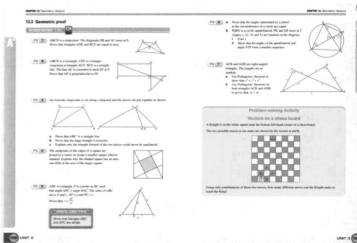 icon.

Examples

Recap on methods you need by reading through the examples before starting the homework exercises.

Functional maths

Practise functional maths skills to see how people use maths in everyday life. Look out for practice questions marked **FM**.

There are also extra functional maths and problem-solving activities at the end of every chapter to build and apply your skills.

New Assessment Objectives

Practise new parts of the curriculum (Assessment Objectives AO2 and AO3) with questions that assess your understanding marked **AU** and questions that test if you can solve problems marked **PS**. You will also practise some questions that involve several steps and where you have to choose which method to use; these also test AO2. There are also plenty of straightforward questions (AO1) that test if you can do the maths.

Student Book CD-ROM

Remind yourself of the work covered in class with the Student Book in electronic form on the CD-ROM. Insert the CD into your machine, click 'Open a PDF file' and choose the chapter you need.

Number: Using a calculator

1.1 Basic calculations and using brackets

HOMEWORK 1A

Use your calculator to work out the following questions. Try to key in the calculation as one continuous set, without writing down any intermediate values.

1 Work out:
  a $(18 - 5) \times 360 \div 24$ **b** $360 - (180 \div 3)$

2 Work out:
  a $\frac{1}{2} \times (6.4 + 9.2) \times 3.6$ **b** $\frac{1}{2} \times (1.7 + 11.5) \times 7.3$

3 Work out the following and give your answers to one decimal place.
  a $\pi \times 7.8$ **b** $2 \times \pi \times 6.1$ **c** $\pi \times 10.2^2$
  d $\pi \times 1.9^2$

FM 4 A monthly travel ticket costs £61.60.
Karen usually spends £4.70 each day on travel.
How many days would she need to travel each month so that it would be cheaper for her to buy a monthly travel ticket?

AU 5 A teacher asked her class to work out: $\dfrac{3.1 + 5.2}{1.9 + 0.3}$

Alfie keyed in:

$\boxed{(}\,\boxed{3}\,\boxed{.}\,\boxed{1}\,\boxed{+}\,\boxed{5}\,\boxed{.}\,\boxed{2}\,\boxed{)}\,\boxed{\div}\,\boxed{1}\,\boxed{.}\,\boxed{9}\,\boxed{+}\,\boxed{0}\,\boxed{.}\,\boxed{3}\,\boxed{=}$

Becky keyed in:

$\boxed{3}\,\boxed{.}\,\boxed{1}\,\boxed{+}\,\boxed{5}\,\boxed{.}\,\boxed{2}\,\boxed{\div}\,\boxed{(}\,\boxed{1}\,\boxed{.}\,\boxed{9}\,\boxed{+}\,\boxed{0}\,\boxed{.}\,\boxed{3}\,\boxed{)}\,\boxed{=}$

Chloe keyed in:

$\boxed{3}\,\boxed{.}\,\boxed{1}\,\boxed{+}\,\boxed{5}\,\boxed{.}\,\boxed{2}\,\boxed{\div}\,\boxed{1}\,\boxed{.}\,\boxed{9}\,\boxed{+}\,\boxed{0}\,\boxed{.}\,\boxed{3}\,\boxed{=}$

Daniel keyed in:

$\boxed{(}\,\boxed{3}\,\boxed{.}\,\boxed{1}\,\boxed{+}\,\boxed{5}\,\boxed{.}\,\boxed{2}\,\boxed{)}\,\boxed{\div}\,\boxed{(}\,\boxed{1}\,\boxed{.}\,\boxed{9}\,\boxed{+}\,\boxed{0}\,\boxed{.}\,\boxed{3}\,\boxed{)}\,\boxed{=}$

They each rounded their answers to three decimal places.
Work out the answer that each of them got.
Who had the correct answer?

PS 6 £1 is equivalent to £1.14 Euros.
£1 is equivalent to 1.49 US dollars ($).
Matt has $100 and 75 Euros.
Which is worth more – the dollars or the Euros?

7 Work out the following if $a = 1.2$, $b = 6.8$ and $c = 7.1$.
  a $ab + c$ **b** $3(ab + ac + bc)$

8 Work out:

a $\sqrt{(0.8^2 + 1.5^2)}$ b $\sqrt{(5.2^2 - 2^2)}$

9 Work out:

a $6.5^3 \times 2 - 2 \times 8.1$

b $2.66^3 - 3 \div 0.15 + 6.4$

1.2 Adding and subtracting fractions with a calculator

HOMEWORK 1B

1 Use your calculator to work out the following.

Try to key in the calculation as one continuous set, without writing down any intermediate values.

Give your answers as mixed fractions.

a $5\frac{1}{4} + 7\frac{3}{5}$ b $8\frac{2}{3} + 1\frac{4}{9}$ c $6\frac{3}{4} + 2\frac{7}{10}$

d $9\frac{1}{8} + 3\frac{7}{25}$ e $7\frac{9}{20} + 3\frac{5}{16}$ f $8\frac{3}{8} + 1\frac{3}{16} + 2\frac{3}{4}$

g $6\frac{17}{20} - 5\frac{5}{12}$ h $2\frac{5}{8} - 1\frac{7}{24}$ i $3\frac{9}{32} - 1\frac{1}{12}$

j $4\frac{3}{5} + 5\frac{7}{16} - 8\frac{1}{3}$ k $1\frac{9}{24} + 1\frac{5}{18} - 1\frac{1}{10}$ l $5\frac{1}{4} + 2\frac{7}{9} - 6\frac{5}{13}$

AU 2 A tank of water is empty. Two-thirds of a full tank is poured in. One-quarter of a full tank is poured out. One-twelfth of a full tank is poured in.

What fraction of the tank is now full of water?

3 Look at this road sign.

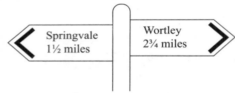

a What is the distance between Springvale and Wortley using these roads?

b How much further is it to Wortley than to Springvale?

AU 4 Here is a calculation:

$\frac{1}{4} \times \frac{2}{3}$

Imagine that you are trying to explain to someone how to do this using a calculator.

Write down what you would say.

PS 5 A class has the same numbers of boys and girls.

Three girls leave and three boys join the class.

The fraction of the class who are girls is now $\frac{3}{8}$.

How many are in the class?

AU 6 a Use your calculator to work out $\frac{19}{23} - \frac{21}{25}$.

b Explain how your answer tells you that $\frac{19}{23}$ is less than $\frac{21}{25}$.

AU 7 a Work out $\frac{10}{27} - \frac{3}{11}$ on your calculator.

b Work out $\frac{10}{27} - \frac{7}{16}$ on your calculator.

c Explain why your answers to parts **a** and **b** show that $\frac{10}{27}$ is a fraction in between $\frac{3}{11}$ and $\frac{7}{16}$.

8 To work out the circumference of a circle, the following formula is used.
$$C = \pi d$$
where d is the diameter.
Work out the circumference of a circle when the diameter is 9 cm.

PS 9 A shape is rotated 30° clockwise and then 90° anticlockwise.
What fraction of a turn is needed to return it to its original position?
Give both possible answers.

1.3 Multiplying and dividing fractions with a calculator

HOMEWORK 1C

1 Use your calculator to work out the following.
Try to key in the calculation as one continuous set, without writing down any intermediate values.
Give your answers as fractions.

  a $\frac{1}{4} \times \frac{3}{5}$ **b** $\frac{2}{3} \times \frac{4}{9}$ **c** $\frac{3}{4} \times \frac{7}{10}$

  d $\frac{1}{8} \times \frac{7}{25}$ **e** $\frac{9}{20} \times \frac{5}{16}$ **f** $\frac{3}{8} \times \frac{3}{16} \times \frac{3}{4}$

  g $\frac{17}{20} \div \frac{5}{12}$ **h** $\frac{5}{8} \div \frac{7}{24}$ **i** $\frac{9}{32} \div \frac{1}{12}$

  j $\frac{3}{5} \times \frac{7}{16} \div \frac{1}{3}$ **k** $\frac{9}{24} \times \frac{5}{18} \div \frac{1}{10}$ **l** $\frac{1}{4} \times \frac{7}{9} \div \frac{5}{13}$

2 The formula for the area of a rectangle is:
    Area = length × width
Use this formula to work the area of a rectangle of length $\frac{3}{4}$ metres and width $\frac{1}{3}$ metres.

3 Bricks are $\frac{1}{6}$ metre long.
How many bricks placed end to end would be needed to make a line two metres long?

AU 4   **a** Use your calculator to work out $\frac{2}{3} \times \frac{7}{11}$ **b** Write down the answer to $\frac{2}{11} \times \frac{7}{3}$

AU 5   **a** Use your calculator to work out $\frac{3}{4} \div \frac{7}{12}$ **b** Use your calculator to work out $\frac{3}{4} \times \frac{12}{7}$

  c Use your calculator to work out $\frac{2}{9} \div \frac{2}{3}$ **d** Write down the answer to $\frac{2}{9} \times \frac{3}{2}$

6 Use your calculator to work out the following questions. Try to key in the calculation as one continuous set, without writing down any intermediate values.
Give your answers as mixed fractions.

  a $3\frac{1}{4} \times 2\frac{3}{5}$ **b** $6\frac{2}{3} \times 1\frac{4}{9}$ **c** $7\frac{3}{4} \times 2\frac{7}{10}$

  d $5\frac{1}{8} \times 2\frac{7}{25}$ **e** $6\frac{9}{20} \times 4\frac{5}{16}$ **f** $1\frac{3}{8} \times 1\frac{3}{16} \times 1\frac{3}{4}$

  g $4\frac{17}{20} \div 2\frac{5}{12}$ **h** $1\frac{5}{8} \div 1\frac{7}{24}$ **i** $2\frac{9}{32} \div 1\frac{1}{12}$

  j $3\frac{3}{5} \times 2\frac{7}{16} \div 1\frac{1}{3}$ **k** $2\frac{9}{24} \times 3\frac{5}{18} \div 1\frac{1}{10}$ **l** $4\frac{1}{4} \times 3\frac{7}{9} \div 2\frac{5}{13}$

7 The formula for the area of a rectangle is:
    Area = length × width
Use this formula to work the area of a rectangle of length $4\frac{3}{4}$ metres and width $2\frac{1}{3}$ metres.

8 The volume of a sphere is $19\frac{2}{5}$ cm³. It is cut into four equal pieces.
Work out the volume of one of the pieces.

9 The formula for average speed is:
    Average speed = Distance ÷ time taken
Work out the average speed of a car which travels $6\frac{3}{4}$ miles in a $\frac{1}{4}$ of an hour.

10 Given that 1 gallon = $4\frac{1}{2}$ litres
Grace puts 40 litres of fuel in her car.
How many gallons is this?
Give your answer to the nearest gallon.

PS FM **11** Ropes come in $12\frac{1}{2}$ metre lengths. Jack wants to cut pieces of rope that are each $\frac{3}{8}$ of a metre long.
He needs 100 pieces.
How many ropes will he need?

Functional Maths Activity

Calculating a gas bill

The following information is written on the back of Mr Fermat's gas bill.

Reading on 19th Aug   05979
Reading on 19th Nov   06229

　　　　　　　　　　= 250 metric units used over 93 days

Gas units converted　= 2785.52 kWh used over 93 days

　　　　　First 683.00 kWh × 6.683p　　　£45.64
　　　　　Next 2102.52 kWh × 3.292p　　　£69.21

　　　　　Total cost of gas used　　　　£114.85

Gas units are converted to kilowatt hours (kWh) using the following formula:

Metric units used	calorific value correction	volume	to convert to kWh	gas used in kWh
250	× 39.2236	× 1.02264	÷ 3.6	= 2785.52

Mr Fermat is having trouble understanding this and has asked for your help. Can you answer these questions for him?

1　Where does the figure of 250 units come from?
2　What does kWh stand for?
3　There are two different prices for gas. The first 683.00 kWh used are charged at a higher rate than the 2102.52 kWh used after that. What are the two different prices for each kWh?
4　Can you check that the formula at the bottom has been worked out correctly: does 250 metric units convert to 2785.52 kWh of gas used?
5　What is the average cost per day of the gas Mr Fermat has used?
6　In fact, the reading taken on 19th November was an estimate because Mr Fermat was out when the meter reader called. When Fermat looks at the meter, the reading is only 06203. By how much has he been overcharged?
7　Mr Fermat informs the gas company of the correct reading and they recalculate his bill. What is the percentage reduction in his bill?

Algebra: Equations and formulae

2.1 Basic algebra

HOMEWORK 2A

1 Find the value of $4x + 3$ when   **a** $x = 3$ **b** $x = 6$ **c** $x = 11$

2 Find the value of $3k - 1$ when   **a** $k = 2$ **b** $k = 5$ **c** $k = 10$

3 Find the value of $4 + t$ when   **a** $t = 5$ **b** $t = 8$ **c** $t = 15$

4 Evaluate $14 - 3f$ when   **a** $f = 4$ **b** $f = 6$ **c** $f = 10$

5 Evaluate $\dfrac{4d - 7}{2}$ when   **a** $d = 2$ **b** $d = 5$ **c** $d = 15$

6 Find the value of $5x + 2$ when   **a** $x = -2$ **b** $x = -1$ **c** $x = 21.5$

7 Evaluate $4w - 3$ when   **a** $w = -2$ **b** $w = -3$ **c** $w = 2.5$

8 Evaluate $10 - x$ when   **a** $x = -3$ **b** $x = -6$ **c** $x = 4.6$

9 Find the value of $5t - 1$ when   **a** $t = 2.4$ **b** $t = -2.6$ **c** $t = 0.05$

10 Evaluate $11 - 3t$ when   **a** $t = 2.5$ **b** $t = -2.8$ **c** $t = 0.99$

FM 11 Two of the first recorded units of measurement were the *cubit* and the *palm*.
The cubit is the distance from the fingertip to the elbow and the palm is the distance across the hand.
A cubit is four and a half palms.
The actual length of a cubit varied throughout history, but it is now accepted to be 54 cm.
Noah's Ark is recorded as being 300 cubits long by 50 cubits wide by 30 cubits high.
What are the dimensions of the Ark in metres?

AU 12 In this algebraic magic square, every row, column and diagonal should add up and simplify to $9a + 6b + 3c$.

$3a - 3b + 4c$	$2a + 8b + c$	$4a + b - 2c$
	$3a + 2b + c$	$2a - 2b + 7c$
$2a + 3b + 4c$		$3a + 7b - 2c$

   a Copy and complete the magic square.
   b Calculate the value of the 'magic number' if $a = 2$, $b = 3$ and $c = 4$.

AU 13 The rule for converting degrees Fahrenheit into degrees Celsius is:

$$C = \frac{5}{9}(F - 32)$$

a Use this rule to convert 68 °F into degrees Celsius.

b Which of the following is the rule for converting degrees Celsius into degrees Fahrenheit?

$$F = \frac{9}{5}(C + 32) \qquad F = \frac{5}{9}C + 32 \qquad F = \frac{9}{5}C + 32 \qquad F = \frac{9}{5}C - 32$$

FM 14 The formula for the cost of water used by a household each quarter is:

£32.40 + £0.003 per litre of water used.

A family uses 450 litres of water each day.

a How much is their total bill per quarter? (Take a quarter to be 91 days.)

b The family pay a direct debit of £45 per month towards their electricity costs. By how much will they be in credit or debit after the quarter?

15 Using $x = 17.4$, $y = 28.2$ and $z = 0.6$, work out the value of:

a $x = \dfrac{y}{z}$ **b** $\dfrac{x + y}{z}$ **c** $\dfrac{x}{z} + y$

16 Expand these expressions.

a $3(4 + m)$ **b** $6(3 + p)$ **c** $4(4 - y)$ **d** $3(6 + 7k)$

e $4(3 - 5f)$ **f** $2(4 - 23w)$ **g** $7(g + h)$ **h** $4(2k + 4m)$

i $6(2d - n)$ **j** $y(3y - 21)$ **k** $2g(4g + 3)$ **l** $4h(2h - 3)$

m $3y(4y + 5k)$ **n** $6m^2(3m - p)$ **o** $h(h^3 + 9)$ **p** $5h(h^3 - 2)$

q $2d(4d^2 - d^3)$ **r** $4w(3w^2 + t)$ **s** $3a(5a^2 - b)$ **t** $3h^2(4h + 5g)$

FM 17 An approximate rule for converting degrees Fahrenheit into degrees Celsius is:

$$C = 0.5(F - 30)$$

a Use this rule to convert 22 °F into degrees Celsius.

b Which of the following is an approximate rule for converting degrees Celsius into degrees Fahrenheit?

$$F = 2(C + 30) \qquad F = 0.5(C + 30) \qquad F = 2(C + 15) \qquad F = 2(C - 15)$$

AU 18 Copy the diagram below and draw lines to show which algebraic expressions are equivalent. One line has been drawn for you.

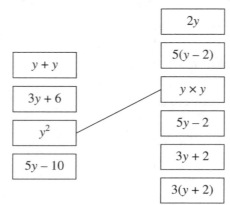

19 Expand and simplify.

a $3(2 + t) + 4(3 + t)$ **b** $6(2 + 3k) + 2(5 + 3k)$ **c** $5(2 + 4m) + 3(1 + 4m)$

d $3(4 + y) + 5(1 + 2y)$ **e** $5(2 + 3f) + 3(6 - f)$ **f** $7(2 + 5g) + 2(3 - g)$

g $4(3 + 2h) - 2(5 + 3h)$ **h** $5(3g + 4) - 3(2g + 5)$ **i** $3(4y + 5) - 2(3y + 2)$

j $3(5t + 2) - 2(4t + 5)$ **k** $5(5k + 2) - 2(4k - 3)$ **l** $4(4e + 3) - 2(5e - 4)$

m $m(5 + p) + p(2 + m)$ **n** $k(4 + h) + h(5 + 2k)$ **o** $t(1 + 2n) + n(3 + 5t)$

p $p(5q + 1) + q(3p + 5)$ **q** $2h(3 + 4j) + 3j(h + 4)$ **r** $3y(4t + 5) + 2t(1 + 4y)$

s $t(2t + 5) + 2t(4 + t)$ **t** $3y(4 + 3y) + y(6y - 5)$ **u** $5w(3w + 2) + 4w(3 - w)$

v $4p(2p + 3) - 3p(2 - 3p)$ **w** $4m(m - 1) + 3m(4 - m)$ **x** $5d(3 - d) + d(2d - 1)$

y $5a(3b + 2a) + a(2a^2 + 3c)$ **z** $4y(3w + y^2) + y(3y - 4t)$

20 **a** Laser printer cartridges cost £75 and print approximately 2500 pages. Approximately how many pence per page does it cost to run, taking only ink consumption into consideration?

b A printing specialist uses a laser printer of this type. He charges a fixed rate of £4.50 to set up the design and five pence for every page.
Explain why his profit on a print run of x pages is, in pounds, $4.5 + 0.02x$

c How much profit will the printing specialist make if he prints 2000 race entry forms for a running club?

PS 21 The expansion $3(4x + 8y) = 12x + 24y$.
Write down two other expansions that give an answer of $12x + 24y$.

FM 22 Adult tickets for a concert cost £x and children's tickets cost £y.
At the afternoon show there were 40 adults and 160 children.
At the evening show there were 60 adults and 140 children.

a Write down an expression for the total amount of money taken on that day in terms of x and y.

b The daily expense for putting on the show is £2200. If $x = 12$ and $y = 9$, how much profit did the theatre make that day?

AU 23 Don wrote the following:
$2(3x - 1) + 5(2x + 3) = 5x - 2 + 10x + 15 = 15x - 13$
Don has made two mistakes in his working.
Explain the mistakes that Don has made.

PS 24 An internet site sells CDs. They cost £$(x + 0.75)$ each for the first five and then £$(x + 0.25)$ for any orders over five.

a Moe buys eight CDs. Which of the following expressions represents how much Moe will pay?

   i $8(x + 0.75)$ **ii** $5(x + 0.75) + 3(x + 0.25)$

   iii $3(x + 0.75) + 5(x + 0.25)$ **iv** $8(x + 0.25)$

b If $x = 5$, how much will Moe pay?

2.2 Solving linear equations

HOMEWORK 2B

1 Solve the following equations.

  a $\dfrac{g}{3} + 2 = 8$ **b** $\dfrac{m}{4} - 5 = 2$ **c** $\dfrac{f}{6} + 3 = 12$ **d** $\dfrac{h}{8} - 3 = 5$

  e $\dfrac{2h}{3} + 3 = 7$ **f** $\dfrac{3t}{4} - 3 = 6$ **g** $\dfrac{2d}{5} + 3 = 18$ **h** $\dfrac{3x}{4} - 1 = 8$

  i $\dfrac{x + 5}{3} = 2$ **j** $\dfrac{t + 12}{2} = 5$ **k** $\dfrac{w - 3}{5} = 3$ **l** $\dfrac{y - 9}{2} = 3$

2 Solve the following equations. Give your answers as fractions or decimals as appropriate.

  a $3(x + 6) = 15$ **b** $6(x - 5) = 30$ **c** $4(t + 3) = 20$

  d $5(4x + 3) = 45$ **e** $3(4y - 7) = 15$ **f** $4(5x + 2) = 88$

  g $3(4t + 2) = 18$ **h** $3(4t + 5) = 51$ **i** $4(6x + 5) = 8$

  j $5(3y - 1) = 10$ **k** $5(2k + 3) = 35$ **l** $5(2x + 8) = 30$

  m $3(2y - 7) = 21$ **n** $3(2t - 5) = 27$ **o** $8(2x - 7) = 16$

  p $8(3x - 4) = 16$ **q** $4(x + 7) = 8$ **r** $3(x - 5) = -24$

  s $5(t + 3) = 15$ **t** $4(3x - 13) = 8$ **u** $5(4t + 3) = 20$

  v $2(5x - 3) = -16$ **w** $4(6y - 8) = -8$ **x** $3(2x + 7) = 9$

3 Solve each of the following equations.

  a $3x + 4 = x + 6$ **b** $4y + 3 = 2y + 5$ **c** $5a - 2 = 2a + 4$

  d $6t + 5 = 2t + 25$ **e** $8p - 3 = 3p + 12$ **f** $5k + 4 = 2k + 13$

FM 4 A rectangular room is four metres longer than it is wide. The perimeter is 28 metres.
It cost £607.50 to carpet the room.
How much is the carpet per square metre?

AU 5 Mike has been asked to solve the equation $a(bx + c) = 60$
Mike knows that the values of a, b and c are 2, 4 and 5, but he doesn't know which
is which.
He also knows that the answer is an even number.
What are the correct values of a, b and c?

PS 6 As the class are coming in for the start of a mathematics lesson, the teacher is writing
some equations on the board.
So far she has written:

    $5(2x + 3) = 13$
    $2(5x + 3) = 13$

Zak says, "That's easy – both equations have the same solution, $x = 2$."
Is Zak correct? If not, then what mistake has he made? What are the correct answers?

7 Solve each of the following equations.

  a $2(d + 4) = d + 15$ **b** $4(x - 3) = 3(x + 3)$ **c** $2(3y + 2) = 5(2y - 4)$

  d $3(2b - 1) + 25 = 4(3b + 1)$ **e** $3(4c + 1) - 17 = 2(3c + 2) - 3c$

AU 8 The solution to the equation $\dfrac{3x}{4} + 3 = 9$ is $x = 8$.

Make up **two** more **different** equations of the form $\dfrac{ax}{b} \pm c = d$, where a, b, c and d are

positive whole numbers, for which the answer is also 8.

9 Solve the following equations.

a $\dfrac{2x-1}{3} = 5$ **b** $\dfrac{5t-4}{2} = 3$ **c** $\dfrac{4m+1}{5} = 5$ **d** $\dfrac{8p-6}{5} = 2$

e $\dfrac{5x+1}{4} = 4$ **f** $\dfrac{17+2t}{9} = 1$ **g** $\dfrac{2+4x}{3} = 4$ **h** $\dfrac{8-2x}{11} = 1$

FM 10 A party of eight friends went for a meal in a restaurant. The bill was £x. They received a £2 per person reduction on the bill.
They split the bill between them. Each person paid £11.25.
a Set this problem up as an equation.
b Solve the equation to work out the bill before the reduction.

2.3 Setting up equations

HOMEWORK 2C

Set up an equation to represent each situation described below. Then solve the equation.
Do not forget to check each answer.

PS 1 A girl is Y years old. Her father is 23 years older than she is. The sum of their ages is 37. How old is the girl?

PS 2 A boy is X years old. His sister is twice as old as he is. The sum of their ages is 24. How old is the boy?

PS 3 The diagram shows a rectangle.
Find x if the perimeter is 24 cm.

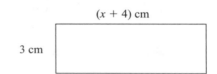

PS 4 Find the length of each side of the pentagon, if it has a perimeter of 32 cm.

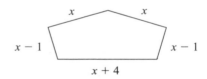

PS 5 On a bookshelf there are $2b$ crime novels, $3b - 2$ science fiction novels and $b + 7$ romance novels. Find how many of each type of book there is, if there are 65 books altogether.

PS 6 Maureen thought of a number. She multiplied it by 4 and then added 6 to get an answer of 26. What number did she start with?

PS 7 Declan also thought of a number. He took 4 from the number and then multiplied by 3 to get an answer of 24. What number did he start with?

FM 8 Books cost twice as much as magazines.
Kerry buys the same number of books and magazines and pays £22.50.
Derek buys one book and two magazines and pays £6.
How many magazines did Kerry buy?

FM 9 Sandeep's money box contains 50p coins, £1 coins and £2 coins.
In the box there are twice as many £1 coins as 50p coins and 4 more £2 coins than 50p coins. There are 44 coins in the box.
a Find how many of each coin there are in the box.
b How much money does Sandeep have in her money box?

2.4 Trial and improvement

HOMEWORK 2D

1 Find two consecutive whole numbers between which the solution to each of the following equations lies.

a $x^3 + x = 7$ **b** $x^3 + x = 55$ **c** $x^3 + x = 102$ **d** $x^3 + x = 89$

2 Find a solution to each of the following equations to 1 decimal place.

a $x^3 - x = 30$ **b** $x^3 - x = 95$ **c** $x^3 - x = 150$ **d** $x^3 - x = 333$

3 Show that $x^3 + x = 45$ has a solution between $x = 3$ and $x = 4$, and find the solution to 1 decimal place.

4 Show that $x^3 - 2x = 95$ has a solution between $x = 4$ and $x = 5$, and find the solution to 1 decimal place.

5 A rectangle has an area of 200 cm². Its length is 8 cm longer than its width. Find the dimensions of the rectangle, correct to 1 decimal place.

6 A gardener wants his rectangular lawn to be 15 m longer than the width, and the area of the lawn to be 800 m². What are the dimensions he should make his lawn? (Give your solution to 1 decimal place.)

7 A triangle has a vertical height 2 cm longer than its base length. Its area is 20 cm². What are the dimensions of the triangle? (Give your solution to 1 decimal place.)

8 A rectangular picture has a height 3 cm shorter than its length. Its area is 120 cm². What are the dimensions of the picture? (Give your solution to 1 decimal place.)

FM 9 This cuboid has a volume of 1000 cm³.

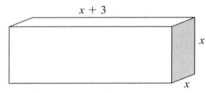

a Write down an expression for the volume.

b Use trial and improvement to find the value of x to 1 decimal place.

AU 10 Darius is using trial and improvement to find a solution to the equation $x^3 - x^2 = 25$.

The table shows his first trial.

x	$x^3 - x^2$	Comment
3	18	Too low

Continue the table to find a solution to the equation. Give your answer to 1 decimal place.

PS 11 Two numbers a and b are such that $ab = 20$ and $a - b = 5$.

Use trial and improvement to find the two numbers to one decimal place.

You can use a table like the one below. The first two lines have been done for you.

a	$b = (20 \div a)$	$a - b$	Comment
5	4	1	Too low
10	2	8	Too high

2.5 Solving simultaneous equations

HOMEWORK 2E

Solve the following simultaneous equations.

1 $3x + 2y = 7$
$5x - 2y = 9$

2 $x + 4y = 2$
$2x - 5y = 17$

3 $3x - 2y = 13$
$4x + 3y = 6$

4 $3x - 4y = 3$
$2x + 5y = 25$

5 $3x + 2y = 21$
$2x + 3y = 19$

6 $5x + 3y = 17$
$7x - 4y = 32$

7 $3x + 2y = 4$
$2x - 3y = 7$

8 $5x - 2y = 16$
$2x - 3y = 2$

2.6 Solving problems with simultaneous equations

HOMEWORK 2F

Read each situation carefully, then make a pair of simultaneous equations in order to solve the problem.

PS 1 A book and a CD cost £14.00 together. The CD costs £7 more than the book. How much does each cost?

PS 2 Ten second-class and six first-class stamps cost £4.96.
Eight second-class and 10 first-class stamps cost £5.84.
How much do I pay for three second-class and four first-class stamps?

3 At the shop, Henri pays £4.37 for six cans of cola and five chocolate bars. On his next visit to the shop he pays £2 for three cans of cola and two chocolate bars. A few days later, he wants to buy two cans of cola and a chocolate bar. How much will they cost him?

FM 4 In her storeroom, Chef Mischa has bags of sugar and rice. The bags are not individually marked, but three bags of sugar and four bags of rice weigh 12 kg. Five bags of sugar and two bags of rice weigh 13 kg.
Help Chef Mischa to work out the weight of two bags of sugar and five bags of rice.

FM 5 Ina wants to buy some snacks for her friends. She works out from the labelling that two cakes and three bags of peanuts contain 63 g of fat; one cake and four bags of peanuts contain 64 g of fat. Help her to work out how many grams of fat there are in each item.

PS 6 The difference between my son's age and my age is 28 years.
Five years ago my age was double that of my son.
Let my age now be x and my son's age now be y.
a Explain why $x - 5 = 2(y - 5)$.
b Find the values of x and y.

FM 7 In a record shop, three CDs and five DVDs cost £77.50.
In the same shop, three CDs and three DVDs cost £55.50.
a Using c to represent the cost of a CD and d to represent the cost of a DVD set up the above information as a pair of simultaneous equations.
b Solve the equations.
c Work out the cost of four CDs and six DVDs.

FM 8 Four apples and two oranges cost £2.04.
Five apples and one orange costs £1.71.
Baz buys four apples and eight oranges.
How much change will he get from a £10 note?

FM 9 Wath School buys basic scientific calculators and graphical calculators to sell to students.
An order for 30 basic scientific calculators and 25 graphical calculators came to a total of £1240. Another order for 25 basic scientific calculators and 10 graphical calculators came to a total of £551.25.
Using £x to represent the cost of basic scientific calculators and £y to represent the cost of graphical calculators, set up and solve a pair of simultaneous equations to find the cost of the next order, for 35 basic scientific calculators and 15 graphical calculators.

FM 10 Five bags of compost and four bags of pebbles weigh 340 kg.
Three bags of compost and five bags of pebbles weigh 321 kg.
Carol wants six bags of compost and eight bags of pebbles.
Her trailer has a safe working load of 500 kg.
Can Carol carry all the bags safely on her trailer?

2.7 Solving quadratic equations

HOMEWORK 2G

Solve the following quadratic equations.

1 $x^2 + 6x - 7 = 0$

2 $x^2 - 8x - 105 = 0$

3 $x^2 - 7x + 12 = 0$

4 $x^2 - 25 = 0$

5 $18x^2 - 2 = 0$

6 $4x^2 + 9x = 0$

7 $x^2 - 6x + 9 = 0 \; x^2 - 6x + 9 = 0$

8 $3x^2 + 8x - 3 = 0$

9 $5x^2 - 11x + 2 = 0$

10 $12x^2 + 4x - 5 = 0$

2.8 The quadratic formula

HOMEWORK 2H

1 Solve the following equations using the quadratic formula. Give your answers to 2 decimal places.

a $3x^2 + x - 5 = 0$ **b** $2x^2 + 4x + 1 = 0$ **c** $x^2 - x - 7 = 0$

d $3x^2 + x - 1 = 0$ **e** $3x^2 + 7x + 3 = 0$ **f** $2x^2 + 11x + 1 = 0$

g $2x^2 + 5x + 1 = 0$ **h** $x^2 + 2x - 9 = 0$ **i** $x^2 + 2x - 6 = 0$

2 Solve the equation $x^2 = 5x + 7$, giving your answers correct to 3 significant figures.

PS 3 A rectangular lawn is 5 m longer than it is wide.

The area of the lawn is 60 m².

How long is the lawn?

Give your answer to the nearest cm.

AU 4 Gerard is solving a quadratic equation using the formula method.

He correctly substitutes values for a, b and c to get $x = \dfrac{4 \pm \sqrt{112}}{6}$

What is the equation that Gerard is trying to solve?

PS 5 Eric uses the quadratic formula to solve: $9x^2 - 12x + 4 = 0$

June uses factorisation to solve: $9x^2 - 12x + 4 = 0$

They both find something unusual in their solutions.

Explain what this is, and why.

2.9 Solving problems with quadratic equations

HOMEWORK 2I

1 Work out the discriminant $b^2 - 4ac$ of the following equations. In each case say how many solutions the equation has.

a $3x^2 + 6x + 3 = 0$ **b** $2x^2 + 3x - 5 = 0$ **c** $2x^2 + 3x + 5 = 0$

d $8x^2 + 3x - 2 = 0$ **e** $5x^2 + 4x + 1 = 0$ **f** $4x^2 + 4x + 1 = 0$

PS 2 Bill works out the discriminant of the quadratic equation $x^2 + bx - c = 0$

as: $b^2 - 4ac = 33$

There are six possible equations that could lead to this discriminant, where a, b and c are integers. What are they?

HOMEWORK 2J

PS 1 The sides of a right-angled triangle are $3x$, $(x + 1)$ and $(4x - 3)$. Find the actual dimensions of the triangle.

PS 2 The length of a rectangle is 3 m more than its width. Its area is 130 m². Find the actual dimensions of the rectangle.

3 Solve the equation: $x + \dfrac{2}{x} = 5$

Give your answers correct to 2 decimal places.

4 Solve the equation: $3x + \dfrac{2}{x} = 7$

PS 5 The area of a triangle is 24 cm². The base is 8 cm longer than the height. Use this information to set up a quadratic equation. Solve the equation to find the length of the base.

FM 6 On a journey of 210 km, the driver of a train calculates that if he were to increase his average speed by 10 km/h, he would take 30 minutes less. Find his average speed.

FM 7 After a 25p per kilogram increase in the price of bananas, I can buy 2 kilograms less for £6 than I could last week. How much do bananas cost this week?

8 Gareth took part in a 26-mile race.
  a He ran the first 15 miles at an average speed of x mph. He ran the last 11 miles at an average speed of $(x - 2)$ mph. Write down an expression, in terms of x, for the time he took to complete the 26-mile race.
  b Gareth took four hours to complete the race. Using your answer to part **a**, form an equation in terms of x.
  c **i** Simplify your equation and show that it can be written as: $2x^2 - 17x + 15 = 0$
     ii Solve the equation and obtain Gareth's average speed over the first 15 miles.

FM 9 Ana, an interior decorator, is told that a rectangular room is 4 m longer than it is wide.
She is also told that it cost £195 to carpet the room.
The cost of the carpet was £12 per square metre.
Help her to work out the width of the room.

Functional Maths Activity

Picture framing

Sam has a photograph that measures 8 cm by 10 cm.

She puts it into a frame that is the same width all the way round.

She notices that the area of the rectangle formed by the frame is twice the area of the original photograph.

How wide is the frame? Explain how you found the answer.

3 Number: Proportions

3.1 Speed, time and distance

HOMEWORK 3A

1 A cyclist travels a distance of 60 miles in 4 hours. What was her average speed?

2 How far along a motorway will you travel if you drive at an average speed of 60 mph for 3 hours?

3 Mr Baylis drives on a business trip from Manchester to London in $4\frac{1}{2}$ hours. The distance he travels is 207 miles. What is his average speed?

4 The distance from Leeds to Birmingham is 125 miles. The train I catch travels at an average speed of 50 mph. If I catch the 11.30 am train from Leeds, at what time would I expect to be in Birmingham?

5 Copy and complete the following table.

	Distance travelled	Time taken	Average speed
a	240 miles	8 hours	
b	150 km	3 hours	
c		4 hours	5 mph
d		$2\frac{1}{2}$ hours	20 km/h
e	1300 miles		400 mph
f	90 km		25 km/h

6 A coach travels at an average speed of 60 km/h for 2 hours on a motorway and then slows down in a town centre to do the last 30 minutes of a journey at an average speed of 20 km/h.
 a What is the total distance of this journey?
 b What is the average speed of the coach over the whole journey?

7 Hilary cycles to work each day. She cycles the first 5 miles at an average speed of 15 mph and then cycles the last mile in 10 minutes.
 a How long does it take Hilary to get to work?
 b What is her average speed for the whole journey?

8 Martha drives home from work in 1 hour 15 minutes. She drives home at an average speed of 36 mph.
 a Change 1 hour 15 minutes to decimal time in hours.
 b How far is it from Martha's work to her home?

PS 9 A tram route takes 15 minutes at an average speed of 16 mph.
 The same journey by car is two miles longer.
 How fast would a car need to travel to arrive in the same time?

FM 10 A taxi travelled for 30 minutes.
 The fare was £24.
 If the fare was charged at £1.20 per mile, what was the average speed of the taxi?

AU 11 Two cars are 30 miles apart but travelling towards each other.
The average speed of one car is twice as fast as the other car.
The slower car is averaging 20 mph.
How long is it before they meet up?

3.2 Direct proportion problems

HOMEWORK 3B

1 If four video tapes cost £3.20, what would 10 video tapes cost?

2 Five oranges cost 90p. Find the cost of 12 oranges.

3 Dylan earns £18.60 in 3 hours. How much will he earn in 8 hours?

4 Barbara bought 12 postcards for 3 euros when she was on holiday in Tenerife.
  a How many euros would she have paid if she had only bought 9 postcards?
  b How many postcards could she have bought with a 5 euro note?

FM 5 Five 'Day-Rover' bus tickets cost £8.50.
  a What is the cost of 16 tickets?
  b Pat has £20. She wants to buy 12 tickets.
    Can she afford them?
    Show your working of how you decide.

6 A car uses 8 litres of petrol on a trip of 72 miles.
  a How much would be used on a trip of 54 miles?
  b How far would the car go on a full tank of 45 litres?

7 It takes a photocopier 18 seconds to produce 12 copies. How long will it take to produce 32 copies?

8 Val has a recipe for making 12 flapjacks.
    100 g margarine
    4 tablespoons golden syrup
    80 g granulated sugar
    200 g rolled oats

FM **a** What is the recipe for:
    i 6 flapjacks   **ii** 24 flapjacks   **iii** 30 flapjacks?

PS **b** What is the maximum number of flapjacks she can make if she has 1 kg of each ingredient?

AU 9 Greg the baker sells bread rolls in pack of 6 for £1. Dom the baker sells bread rolls in packs of 24 for £3.19.
I have £5 to spend on bread rolls.
How many more can I buy from Greg than from Dom?

FM 10 To make white coffee, one-quarter of a cup is filled with milk.
A cup holds 600 ml of white coffee altogether.
How many cups of coffee can be made if you have 1 litre of milk?

PS 11 A nurse can examine 20 patients each hour.
There are 170 patients visiting a three-hour clinic.
How many nurses are needed?

3.3 Best buys

HOMEWORK 3C

FM 1 Compare the prices of the following pairs of products and state which, if any, is the better buy.

a   Mouthwash: £1.99 for a twin pack, or £1.49 each with a 3 for 2 offer.

b   Dusters: 79p for a pack of 6 with a 'buy one pack and get one pack free' offer, or £1.20 for a pack of 20.

2 Compare the following pairs of products and state which is the better buy and why.

a   Tomato ketchup: a medium bottle which is 200 g for 55p or a large bottle which is 350 g for 87p.

b   Milk chocolate: a 125 g bar at 77p or a 200 g bar at 92p.

c   Coffee: a 750 g tin at £11.95 or a 500 g tin at £7.85.

d   Honey: a large jar which is 900 g for £2.35 or a small jar which is 225 g for 65p.

3 Boxes of 'Wetherels' teabags are sold in three different sizes.

Small
80 teabags
£1.44

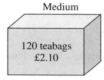
Medium
120 teabags
£2.10

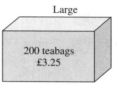
Large
200 teabags
£3.25

Which size box of teabags gives the best value for money?

4 Bottles of 'Cola' are sold in different sizes. Copy and complete the table.

Size of bottle	Price	Cost per litre
$\frac{1}{2}$ litre	36p	
$1\frac{1}{2}$ litres	99p	
2 litres	£1.40	
3 litres	£1.95	

Which size of bottle gives the best value for money?

AU 5 The following 'special offers' were being promoted by a supermarket.

Only £1.99 each
Cornflakes
750 g
£1.99

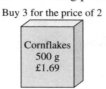
Buy 3 for the price of 2
Cornflakes
500 g
£1.69

Which offer is the better value for money? Explain why.

PS 6 Hannah scored 17 out of 20 in a test. John scored 40 out of 50 in a test of the same standard.

Who got the better mark?

3.4 Density

HOMEWORK 3D

B

1 Find the density of a piece of wood weighing 135 g and having a volume of 150 cm^3.

2 Calculate the density of a metal if 40 cm^3 of it weighs 2500 g.

3 Calculate the weight of a piece of plastic, 25 cm^3 in volume, if its density is 1.2 g/cm^3.

4 Calculate the volume of a piece of wood that weighs 350 g and has a density of 0.7 g/cm^3.

5 Find the weight of a statue, 540 cm^3 in volume, if the density of marble is 2.5 g/cm^3.

6 Calculate the volume of a liquid weighing 1 kg and having a density of 1.1 g/cm^3.

7 Find the density of a stone which weighs 63 g and has a volume of 12 cm^3.

PS 8 It is estimated that a huge rock balanced on the top of a mountain has a volume of 120 m^3. The density of the rock is 8.3 g/cm^3. What is the estimated weight of the rock?

9 A 1 kg bag of flour has a volume of about 900 cm^3. What is the density of flour in g/cm^3?

AU 10 1 m^3 = 1 000 000 cm^3

A storage area has 30 tonnes of sandstone.

The density of some sandstone is 2.3 g/cm^3

a What is the volume of sandstone in the storage area?
Give your answer in m^3.

b The density of granite is 2.7 g/cm^3.
The same volume of granite is stored as the volume of sandstone.
How much heavier is the granite?

AU 11 The density of a piece of oak is 630 kg/m^3.
The density of a piece of mahogany is 550 kg/m^3.
Two identical carvings are made, one from oak and the other from mahogany.
The oak carving has a mass of 315 grams.
What is the mass of the mahogany carving?

FM 12 Two identical-looking metal objects are side by side.
They have different masses.
How does this tell you that they are probably made from different metals?

PS 13 Metal A has density that is half the density of metal B.

Functional Maths Activity

Metal objects

You run a charity shop and the items listed in the table below have been donated. You have estimated their volume in cubic centimetres. Now you need to price them. The second table provides data about the density of metal and the cost per gram.

Use the information to work out the value of each item.

How much would you price each item at and why?

Item	Volume (cm³)
Candlestick (brass)	6
Statue (cast iron)	15
Ring (gold)	0.5
Tankard (Stainless steel)	4
Jug (silver)	3
Plate (Copper)	7

Metal	Density (g/cm³)	Cost per gram
Brass	8.5	29p
Copper	8.9	22p
Gold	19.3	£16.58
Silver	10.4	80p
Stainless steel	7.5	33p
Cast iron	7.2	83p

4 Geometry: Shapes

4.1 Circumference and area of a circle

HOMEWORK 4A

1 Find the circumference of each of the following circles, round off your answers to 1 dp.
  a Diameter 3 cm
  b Radius 5 cm
  c Radius 8 m
  d Diameter 14 cm
  e Diameter 6.4 cm
  f Radius 3.5 cm

2 John runs twice round a circular track which has a radius of 50 m. How far has he run? Give your answers in terms of π.

3 A rolling pin has a diameter of 5 cm.
  a What is the circumference of the rolling pin?
  b How many revolutions does it make when rolling a length of 30 cm?

4 How many complete revolutions will a bicycle wheel with a radius of 28 cm make in a journey of 3 km?

5 Calculate the area of each of these circles, giving your answers to 1 decimal place, except for **a** and **d**, where your answer should be in terms of π.
  a Radius 4 cm
  b Diameter 14 cm
  c Radius 9 cm
  d Diameter 2 m
  e Radius 21 cm
  f Diameter 0.9 cm

6 What is the total perimeter of a semicircle of diameter 7 cm? Give your answer to 1 dp.

7 What is the total perimeter of a semicircle of radius 6 cm? Give your answer in terms of π.

8 A circle has a circumference of 12 cm. What is its diameter?

9 A garden has a circular lawn of diameter 20 m. There is a path 1 m wide all the way round the circumference. What is the area of this path?

10 Calculate the area of a semicircle with a diameter of 15 cm. Give your answer to 1 dp.

11 A circle has an area of 50 m². What is its radius?

12 I have a circle with a circumference of 25 cm. What is the area of this circle?

13 Jane walked around a circular lawn. She counted 153 paces to walk round it. Each of her paces was about 42 cm. What is the area of the lawn?

AU 14 Calculate the area of this shape.

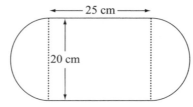

FM 15 The diameter of a cycle wheel is 70 cm. How many metres will the cycle travel if the wheel makes 50 revolutions?

4.2 Area of a trapezium

HOMEWORK 4B

 1 Calculate the perimeter and the area of each of these trapeziums.

a

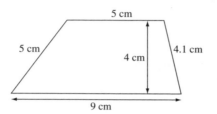

b

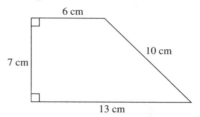

2 Calculate the area of each of these shapes.

a

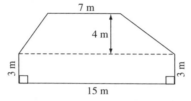

b

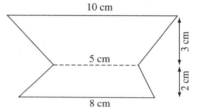

 3 Which of the following shapes has the largest area?

a

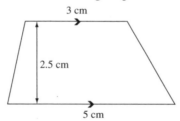

b

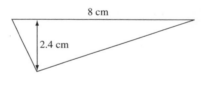

 AU 4 Calculate the area of this trapezium.

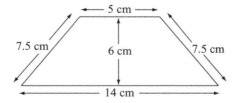

FM 5 This is the plan of an area that is to be seeded with grass.

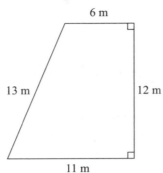

Seed should be planted at a rate of 30 g per m^2.
How much grass seed will be required?

PS 6 A trapezium has an area of 100 cm^2. The parallel sides are 17 cm and 23 cm long.
How far apart are the parallel sides?

7 Calculate the area of the shaded part in each of these diagrams.

a

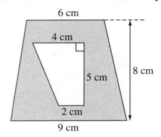

b

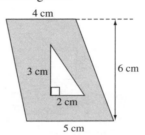

8 What percentage of this shape has been shaded?

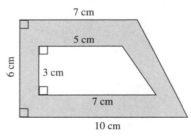

4.3 Sectors

HOMEWORK 4C

 1 For these sectors, calculate the arc length and the sector area.

a

b

2 Calculate the arc length and the area of a sector whose arc subtends a right angle in a
circle of diameter 10 cm. Give your answer in terms of π.

3 Calculate the total perimeter of each of these shapes.

a

20 cm

b

12 cm

 4 Calculate the area of each of these shapes.

a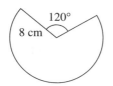

120°
8 cm

b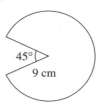

45°
9 cm

 5 There is an infrared sensor in a security system. The sensor can detect movement inside a sector of a circle. The radius of the circle is 16 m. The sector is 120°. Calculate the area of the sector.

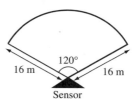

120°
16 m   16 m
Sensor

AU 6 A circle of radius 8 cm is cut up into five congruent sectors. Calculate the perimeter of each one.

FM 7 A shelf to fit in the corner of a room is to be cut in the shape of a quarter of a circle. It will be cut from a square of wood of side 30 cm. What will be the area of the shelf?

PS 8 ABCD is a square of side length 15 cm. APC and AQC are arcs of the circle with centres D and B. Calculate the area of the unshaded part.

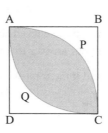

A   B
        P
Q
D   C

4.4 Volume of a prism

HOMEWORK 4D

1 For each prism shown, calculate the area of the cross-section and the volume.

a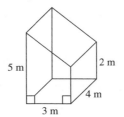

5 m   2 m
            4 m
3 m

b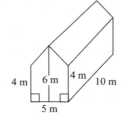

4 m   6 m   4 m   10 m
        5 m

AU 2 A chocolate box is in the form of a triangular prism. It is 18 cm long and has a volume of 387 cm³.
What is the area of the triangular end of the box?

FM 3 A wooden door wedge has a cross-section which is this shape:

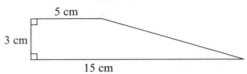

The wedge is 3 cm wide.
a Calculate the volume of wood needed to make the wedge.
b If the wedge is cut from a block of wood (cuboid) measuring 15 cm × 3 cm × 3 cm, what volume of wood is wasted?

AU 4 Which of these solids is:
a the heaviest   **b** the lightest?

i (1.26 g/cm³)   **ii**   **iii**

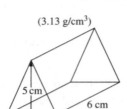

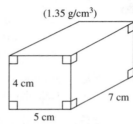

4.5 Cylinders

HOMEWORK 4E

1 Find **i** the volume and **ii** the curved surface area of a cylinder with base radius 5 cm and height 4 cm. Give your answer in terms of π.

2 Find **i** the volume and **ii** the curved surface area of a cylinder with base radius 8 cm and height 17 cm. Give your answer to a suitable degree of accuracy.

3 Find **i** the volume and **ii** the total surface area of each of these cylinders.

a 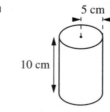   **b**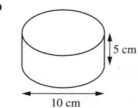

4 What is the radius of a cylinder with a height of 6 cm and a volume of 24π cm³?

5 What is the radius of a cylinder with a height of 10 cm and a curved surface area of 360π cm²?

6 What is the height of a cylinder with a diameter of 12 cm and a volume of 108π cm³?

7 A cylinder of height 20 cm has a curved surface area of 200 cm². Calculate the volume of this cylinder.

8 Calculate the curved surface area of a cylinder which has a height of 18 cm and a volume of 390 cm^3.

9 A cylinder has the same height and radius. The total surface area is 100π. Calculate the volume. Give your answer in terms of π.

AU 10 A square of paper of side 10 cm is bent round to make a cylindrical shape by putting two edges together.
What is the volume of the cylinder?

FM 11 A cylindrical food can must have a volume of at least 400 cm^3 in order to hold the correct amount.
The diameter of the can has to be 7 cm.
What is the smallest possible height of the can?

PS 12 Metal cylinders are made by bending rectangular sheets of metal measuring 15 cm long by 6 cm wide until the sides meet.
How many cylinders can be made from a sheet of metal that is 2 m long and 1 m wide?

4.6 Volume of a pyramid

HOMEWORK 4F

1 Calculate the volume of each of these pyramids, both with rectangular bases.

a
b

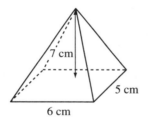
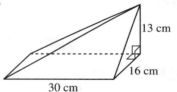

2 Calculate the volume of a pyramid that has a square base of side 10 cm and a vertical height of 18 cm.

AU 3 An octahedron is made by fixing together the two square bases of two identical pyramids.
Each pyramid is 9 cm high and has a base with each side 7 cm.
Calculate the volume of the octahedron.

4 The Khufu pyramid in Egypt was originally 146 m tall.
Each side of the square base was 230 m long.
It was built from limestone blocks with a density of about 2.7 tonnes per cubic metre.
It probably took 20 years to complete.
Estimate the total weight of the blocks used to build the pyramid.

5 Calculate the volume of this shape.

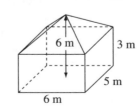

6 Calculate the height h of a rectangular-based pyramid with a length of 14 cm, a width of 10 cm and a volume of 140 cm³.

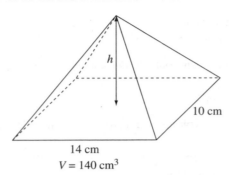

14 cm

10 cm

$V = 140 \text{ cm}^3$

7 The pyramid in the diagram has its top cut off as shown. The shape which is left is called a frustum. Calculate the volume of the frustum.

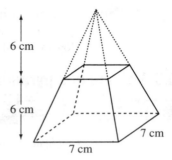

6 cm

6 cm

7 cm

7 cm

4.7 Cones

HOMEWORK 4G

1 For each cone, calculate **i** its volume and **ii** its total surface area. (The units are cm.)

a

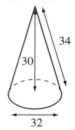

34

30

32

b

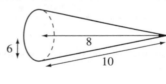

6

8

10

2 Find the total surface area of a cone of which the base radius is 4 cm and slant height is 6 cm. Give your answer in terms of π.

3 Find the volume of a cone of which the base radius is 6 cm and vertical height is 8 cm. Give your answer in terms of π.

4 In order to make a cone, a sector of angle 60° is cut from a circle with a radius of 12 cm.
  a Calculate the circumference of the base of the cone.
  b Calculate the radius of the base of the cone.
  c State the length of the slant height of the cone.
  d Calculate the curved surface area of the cone.
  e Calculate the vertical height of the cone.
  f Calculate the volume of the cone.

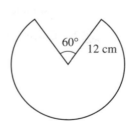

60°

12 cm

AU 5 A cone with a base diameter of 6 cm has the same volume as a cube of side 4 cm. Find the height of the cone.

FM 6 Candy needs to make a conical hat to go with her fancy dress costume.
She knows that the circumference of the hat is 60 cm, and that she has to cut the material in the shape of a sector of a circle.
She also knows that the slant edge of the conical hat is 30 cm.
Help Candy to work out the area of the material she needs to make the hat.

AU 7 A container in the shape of a cone, base radius 10 cm and vertical height 19 cm, is full of water. The water is poured into an empty cylinder of radius 15 cm.
How high is the water in the cylinder?

PS 8 The diagram shows a paper cone. The diameter of the base is 4.8 cm and the slant height is 4 cm. The cone is cut along the line AV and opened out flat, as shown below.

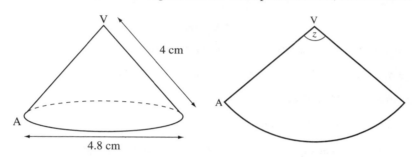

Calculate the size of angle z.

4.8 Spheres

HOMEWORK 4H

1 Calculate the volume of spheres with the following measurements.
Give your answers in terms of π.
a Radius 3 cm **b** Diameter 30 cm

2 Calculate the surface area of spheres with the following measurements.
Give your answers in terms of π.
a Radius 4 cm **b** Diameter 10 cm

3 Calculate the volume and the surface area of a sphere with a diameter of 30 cm.
Give your answers to a suitable degree of accuracy.

4 Calculate, correct to one decimal place, the radius of a sphere:
a with a surface area of 200 cm^2 **b** with a volume of 200 cm^3

5 The volume of a sphere is 50 m^3. Find its diameter.

6 What is the volume of a sphere with a surface area of 400 cm^2?

AU 7 A cube of metal of side 5 cm has a hemispherical hole of diameter 4 cm cut into it.
What is the volume of the resulting shape?

FM 8 A roller skate manufacturing company needs to make 4 mm-diameter steel ball bearings.
How many ball bearings can the company make from one cubic metre of steel?

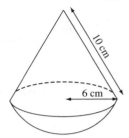

9 A spinning top, which consists of a cone of base radius 6 cm, slant height 10 cm and a hemisphere of radius 6 cm, is illustrated on the right. Give your answers in terms of π.

a Calculate the volume of the spinning top.

b Calculate the total surface area of the spinning top.

Functional Maths Activity

Packaging sweets

A sweets manufacturer wants a new package for an assortment of sweets.

The package must have a volume of 1000 cm³ in order to hold the sweets.

The chosen design will be a prism.

The length has been specified as 20 cm.

The cross-section of the package will be one of three possibilities: a square, an equilateral triangle or a circle.

You have been asked to investigate the amount of packaging material needed for each design, as this will affect the cost of manufacture.

Calculate the surface area of each of the three designs.

Comment on how much difference there is between the three surface areas and how this could affect production costs.

This formula could be useful:

The area of an equilateral triangle of side a is $\dfrac{a^2\sqrt{3}}{4}$

Geometry: Pythagoras and trigonometry

5.1 Pythagoras' theorem

HOMEWORK 5A

1 In each of the following triangles, find the hypotenuse, rounding off to a suitable degree of accuracy.

a
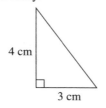
4 cm
3 cm

b
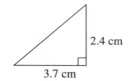
2.4 cm
3.7 cm

c

5.6 cm
9 cm

d
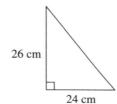
26 cm
24 cm

e
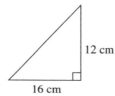
12 cm
16 cm

f
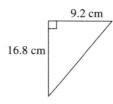
9.2 cm
16.8 cm

2 This diagram shows the cross-section of a swimming pool 50 m long. It is 3.5 m deep at the deep end. The deepest part of the pool is 10 m long. It is not drawn to scale.

a Calculate the length of the sloping bottom of the pool AB.

b The pool is 20 m wide. What is its volume?

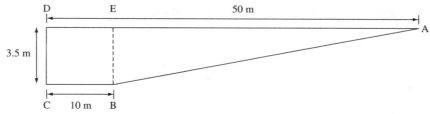

AU 3 Three of these lengths could form the sides of a right-angled triangle:

7.5 cm   10 cm   12.5 cm   15 cm

Which one would not be used? Give a reason for your answer.

FM 4 A beam of wood is needed to support a sloping roof, as shown. The beam spans a horizontal distance of 3.50 m and the difference between the bottom and the top is 1.50 m.

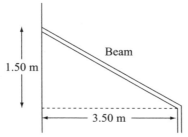
Beam
1.50 m
3.50 m

A builder has a beam that is 4 m long.
Is it long enough?

FM Functional Maths   **AU** (AO2) Assessing Understanding   **PS** (AO3) Problem Solving

5.2 Finding a shorter side

HOMEWORK 5B

1 In each of the following triangles, find the length of x to a suitable degree of accuracy.

a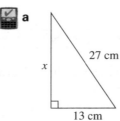

27 cm
x
13 cm

b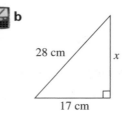

28 cm
x
17 cm

c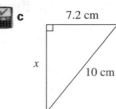

7.2 cm
x
10 cm

d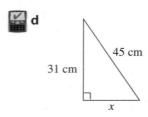

45 cm
31 cm
x

e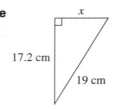

x
17.2 cm
19 cm

f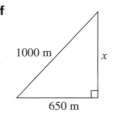

1000 m
x
650 m

g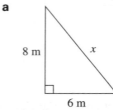

x
2 cm
1.8 cm

h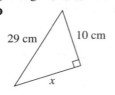

13 m
x
5 m

2 In each of the following triangles, find the length of x to a suitable degree of accuracy.

a

8 m
x
6 m

b

29 cm
10 cm
x

c

15 m
33 m
x

d

9.5 cm
x
8 cm

AU 3 The diagram shows the end view of the framework for a sports arena stand. Calculate the length AB.

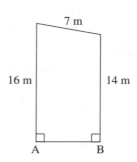

7 m
16 m
14 m
A
B

4 Calculate the lengths of a and b.

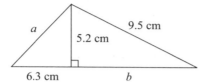

 FM **5** A ladder 3.8 m long is placed against a wall. The foot of the ladder is 1.1 m from the wall.
A window cleaner can reach windows that are 1 m above the top of her ladder. Can she reach a window that is 4 m above the ground?

6 The lengths of the three sides of a right-angled triangle are all a whole number of centimetres. The hypotenuse is 15 cm. How long are the two other sides?

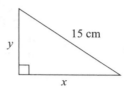

5.3 Applying Pythagoras' theorem in real situations

HOMEWORK 5C

1 A ladder, 15 m long, leans against a wall. The ladder needs to reach a height of 12 m. How far should the foot of the ladder be placed from the wall?

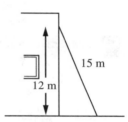

2 A rectangle is 3 m long and 1.2 m wide. How long is the diagonal?

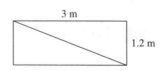

3 How long is the diagonal of a square with a side of 10 m?

4 A ship going from a port to a lighthouse steams 8 km east and 6 km north. How far is the lighthouse from the port?

5 At the moment, three towns, A, B and C, are joined by two roads, as in the diagram. The council wants to make a road that runs directly from A to C. How much distance will the new road save compared to the two existing roads?

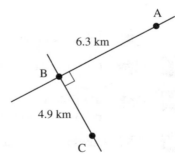

 6 An 8 m ladder is put up against a wall.
   a How far up the wall will it reach when the foot of the ladder is 1 m away from the wall?
   b When it reaches 7 m up the wall, how far is the foot of the ladder away from the wall?

7 How long is the line that joins the two points A(1, 3) and B(2, 2)?

8 A rectangle is 4 cm long. The length of its diagonal is 5 cm. What is the area of the rectangle?

9 Is the triangle with sides 11 cm, 60 cm and 61 cm a right-angled triangle?

10 How long is the line that joins the two points A(−3, −7) and B(4, 6)?

AU 11 The diagram shows a voyage from position A to position B. The boat sails due east from A for 27 km to position C. The boat then changes course and sails for 30 km due south to position B. On a map, the distance between A and C is 10.8 cm.
  a What is the scale of the map?
  b What is the distance from A to B in kilometres?

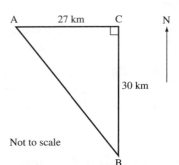

AU 12 A mobile phone mast is supported by a cable that stretches from the top of the mast down to the ground. The mast is 12.5 m high and the cable is 17.8 m long.
How far from the bottom of the mast is the end of the cable that is attached to the ground?

FM 13 A rolling pin is 45 cm long.
Will it fit inside a kitchen drawer which is internally 40 cm long and 33 cm wide?
Justify your answer.

HOMEWORK 5D

1 Calculate the area of these isosceles triangles.

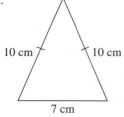
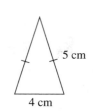

2 Calculate the area of an isosceles triangle with sides of 10 cm, 10 cm and 8 cm.

3 Calculate the area of an equilateral triangle with sides of 10 cm each.

4 **a** Calculate the area of an equilateral triangle with sides of 20 cm each.
  b Explain why the answer to **4a** is not twice that of Question **3**.

5 An isosceles triangle has sides of 6 cm and 8 cm.
  a Sketch the two isosceles triangles that fit this data.
  b Which of the two triangles has the greater area?

6 The diagram shows an isosceles triangle of base 10 mm and side 12 mm. Calculate the area of the triangle.

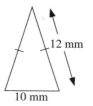

 AU 7 The diagram shows an equilateral triangle drawn inside a square with sides of 10 cm each.

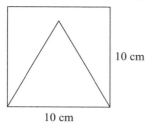

What percentage of the square is outside the triangle?

 FM 8 A picture is hanging on a string secured to two points at the side of the frame.

The string is initially 45 cm long.
When the picture is hung the string stretches as shown.
By how much does the string stretch?

5.4 Pythagoras' theorem in three dimensions

HOMEWORK 5E

1 Is the triangle with sides of 9 cm, 40 cm and 41 cm a right-angled triangle?

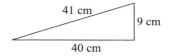

2 A box measures 6 cm by 8 cm by 10 cm.
  a Calculate the lengths of
    i AC **ii** BG **iii** BE
  b Calculate the diagonal distance BH.

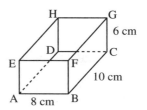

3 A garage is 5 m long, 5 m wide and 2 m high. Can a 7 m long pole be stored in it?

4 Spike, a spider, is at the corner S of the wedge shown in the diagram. Fred, a fly, is at the corner F of the same wedge.
  a Calculate the two distances Spike would have to travel to get to Fred if she used the edges of the wedge.
  b Calculate the distance Spike would have to travel across the face of the wedge to get directly to Fred.

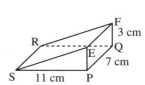

5 A corridor is 5 m wide and turns through a right angle, as in the diagram. What is the longest pole that can be carried along the corridor horizontally? If the corridor is 3 m high, what is the longest pole that can be carried along in any direction?

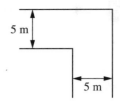

6 For the box shown on the right, find the lengths of:
a   DG
b   HA
c   DB
d   AG

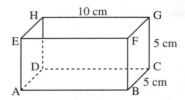

AU 7 A cube has a side of 15 cm.
Calculate the distance between two vertically opposite corners.

FM 8 A small sculpture is made from four equilateral triangles of copper sheet stuck together to make a pyramid.

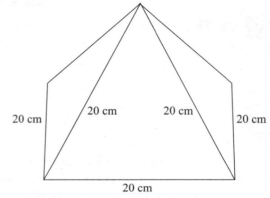

The triangles have a side of 20 cm. How high is the pyramid?

9 The diagram shows a square-based pyramid with base length 7 cm and sloping edges 12 cm. M is the mid-point of the side AB, X is the mid-point of the base, and E is directly above X.
a   Calculate the length of the diagonal AC.
b   Calculate EX, the height of the pyramid.
c   Using triangle ABE, calculate the length EM.

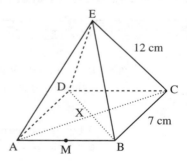

10 Use the answer to Question **1** to find the length of the diagonal AB of the cuboid 9 cm by 9 cm by 40 cm.

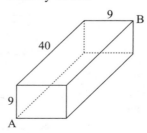

5.5 Trigonometric ratios

HOMEWORK 5F

In these questions, give any answers involving angles to the nearest degree.

1 Find these values, rounding off your answers to 3 significant figures.
    a   sin 52°   **b**   sin 46°   **c**   sin 76.3°   **d**   sin 90°

2 Find these values, rounding off your answers to 3 significant figures.
    a   cos 52°   **b**   cos 46°   **c**   cos 76.3°   **d**   cos 90°

3 **a**   Calculate $(\sin 52°)^2 + (\cos 52°)^2$ **b**   Calculate $(\sin 46°)^2 + (\cos 46°)^2$
    c   Calculate $(\sin 76.3°)^2 + (\cos 76.3°)^2$ **d**   Calculate $(\sin 90°)^2 + (\cos 90°)^2$
    e   What do you notice about your answers?

4 Use your calculator to work out the value of:
    a   tan 52°   **b**   tan 46°   **c**   tan 76.3°   **d**   tan 0°

5 Use your calculator to work out the value of:
    a   sin 52° ÷ cos 52°   **b**   sin 46° ÷ cos 46°   **c**   sin 76.3° ÷ cos 76.3°
    d   sin 0° ÷ cos 0°
    e   What connects your answers with the answers to Question **4**?

6 Use your calculator to work out the value of:
    a   6 sin 55°   **b**   7 cos 45°   **c**   13 sin 67°   **d**   20 tan 38°

7 Use your calculator to work out the value of:
    a $\dfrac{6}{\sin 55°}$ **b** $\dfrac{7}{\cos 45°}$ **c** $\dfrac{13}{\sin 67°}$ **d** $\dfrac{20}{\tan 38°}$

8 Using the following triangle, calculate sin, cos, and tan for the angle marked x.
Leave your answers as fractions.

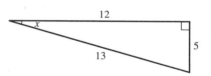

AU 9 You are given that $\sin x = \dfrac{5}{\sqrt{34}}$. Work out the value of tan x.

5.6 Calculating angles

HOMEWORK 5G

Use your calculator to find the answers to the following to one decimal place.

1 What angles have sines of:
    a   0.4   **b**   0.707   **c**   0.879   **d**   0.666666666666666…

2 What angles have cosines of:
    a   0.4   **b**   0.707   **c**   0.879   **d**   0.333333333333333…

3 What angles have the following tangents?
    a   0.4   **b**   1.24   **c**   0.875   **d**   2.625

4 What angles have the following sines?
    a   3 ÷ 8   **b**   1 ÷ 3   **c**   3 ÷ 10   **d**   5 ÷ 8

B

5 What angles have the following cosines?

   a $3 \div 8$ **b** $1 \div 3$ **c** $3 \div 10$ **d** $5 \div 8$

6 What angles have the following tangents?

   a $3 \div 8$ **b** $3 \div 2$ **c** $5 \div 7$ **d** $19 \div 5$

7 If $\sin 54° = 0.809$ to 3 decimal places, what angle has a cosine of 0.809?

5.7 Using the sine and cosine functions

HOMEWORK 5H

B

1 Find the value marked x in each of these diagrams.

   a 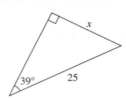   **b** 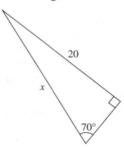   **c**

   d   **e** 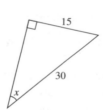   **f**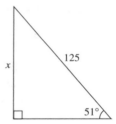

2 Angle θ has a sine of $\frac{7}{20}$. Calculate the missing lengths of these triangles.

   a   **b** 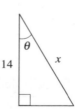   **c**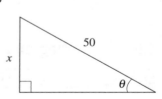

AU **3** Caxton is due north of Ashville and due west of
   Peaton. A pilot flies directly from Ashville to Peaton,
   a distance of 15 km, on a bearing of 050°.

   a Calculate the direct distance from Caxton
      to Peaton.

   b Work out the bearing of Ashville from Peaton.

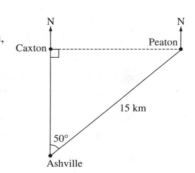

HOMEWORK 5I

1 Find the value marked *x* in each of these triangles.

a

b

c
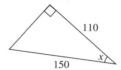

d
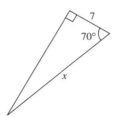

e

f
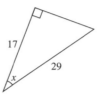

2 Angle θ has a cosine of $\frac{7}{15}$. Calculate the missing lengths of these triangles.

a
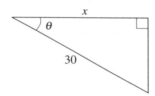

b

c

AU 3 The diagram shows the positions of three telephone masts A, B and C.

Mast C is 6 kilometres due east of Mast B.

Mast A is due north of Mast B, and 9 km from Mast C.

a Calculate the distance of A from B.
Give your answer in kilometres, correct to 3 significant figures.

b Calculate the size of the angle marked *x*.
Give your angle correct to one decimal place.

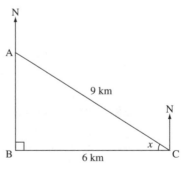

5.8 Using the tangent function

HOMEWORK 5J

1 Find the value marked *x* in each of these triangles.

a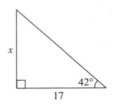

b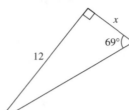

c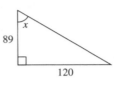

d

e

f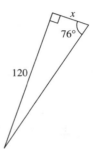

2 Angle θ has a tangent of $\frac{2}{3}$. Calculate the missing lengths of these triangles.

a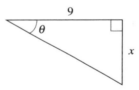

b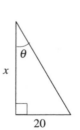

c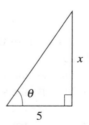

AU 3 The sensor for a security light is fixed to a house wall 2.25 m above the ground. It can detect movement on the ground up to 15 m away from the house. B is the furthest point where the sensor, A, can detect movement.
Calculate the size of angle *x*.

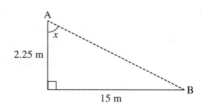

5.9 Which ratio to use

HOMEWORK 5K

1 Find the angle or length marked *x* in each of these triangles.

a

b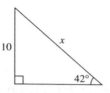

c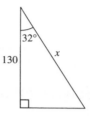

d

e

f

g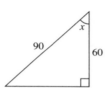

h

i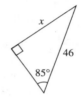

2 The diagram shows a right-angled triangle, ABC.
Angle C = 90° and AB = 10 cm
Given that cos B = 0.8, sin B = 0.6 and tan B = 0.75,
calculate the length of AC.

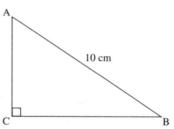

3 A lift at the seaside takes people from sea level
to the top of a cliff, as shown.
From sea level to the top of the cliff, the lift
travels 23 m, to a height of 21 m.
  a Calculate the distance AC. Give your answer
    to an appropriate degree of accuracy.
  b Calculate angle BCA.

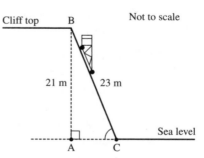

4 Look at this triangle.

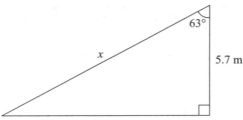

Find the length of side *x*.

5.10 Solving problems using trigonometry 1

HOMEWORK 5L

In these questions, give any answers involving angles to the nearest degree.

1 A ladder, 8 m long, rests against a wall. The foot of the ladder is 2.7 m from the base of the wall. What angle does the ladder make with the ground?

FM 2 The ladder in Question **1** has a 'safe angle' with the ground of between 70° and 80°. What are the safe limits for the distance of the foot of the ladder from the wall?

3 Angela walks 60 m from the base of a block of flats and then measures the angle from the ground to the top of the flats to be 42° as shown in the diagram. How high is the block of flats?

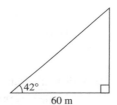

4 A slide is at an angle of 46° to the horizontal. The slide is 7 m long. How high is the top of the slide above the ground?

5 Use trigonometry to calculate the angle that the diagonal makes with the long side of a rectangle 9 cm by 5 cm.

FM 6 Drumsbury Town Council wants to put up a flag pole outside the town hall. The diagram shows the end view of the town hall building.
Regulations state that the flag pole must not be more than half the height of the building.
What is the maximum height that the flag pole can be?

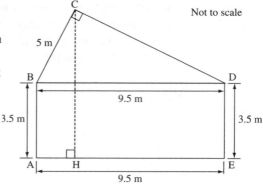

Not to scale

AU 7 A road rises steadily at an angle of 6°. A lorry travels 300 m along the road. What is the increase in height?

FM 8 A swing at rest is 50 cm above the ground and 2 m below the point of suspension. When a child is on the swing, the angle with the vertical can be as large as 35°.

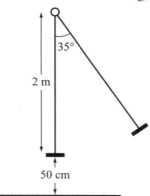

The child's father thinks that she might then be dangerously far from the ground. Can you tell him exactly how far his daughter will be above the ground?

HOMEWORK 5M

In these questions, give any answers involving angles to the nearest degree.

1 Eric sees an aircraft in the sky. The aircraft is at a horizontal distance of 15 km from Eric. The angle of elevation is 42°. How high is the aircraft?

2 A man standing 100 m from the base of a block of flats, looks at the top of the block and notices that the angle of elevation is 49°. How high is the block of flats?

3 A man stands 15 m from a tree. The angle of elevation of the top of the tree from his eye is 25°. If his eye is 1.5 m above the ground, how tall is the tree?

4 A bird, sitting at the very top of the tree in Question **3**, sees a worm next to the foot of the man. What is the angle of depression from the bird's eye to the worm?

5 I walk 200 m away from a chimney that is 120 m high. What is the angle of elevation from my eye to the top of the chimney? (Ignore the height of my eye above the ground.)

6 If you are now told that the height of my eye in Question **5** is 1.8 m above ground, how much different is the angle of elevation?

AU 7 Boat B is moored 50 m from the foot of a vertical cliff. The angle of depression of the boat from the top of the cliff is 52°.
   a Calculate the height of the cliff.
   b The boat is released from its mooring and it drifts 350 m further away from the cliff. Calculate the angle of elevation of the top of the cliff from the boat.

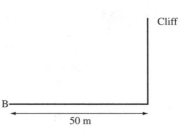

8 A boat is 450 m from the base of a cliff.
The angle of elevation of the top of the cliff is 8°.
How high is the cliff?

FM **9** To find the height of a tree, Sacha tries to measure the angle of elevation of the top from a point 40 m away.

He finds it difficult to measure the angle accurately, but thinks it is between 30° and 35°.
What can you tell him about the height of the tree?

5.11 Solving problems using trigonometry 2

HOMEWORK 5N

1 A ship sails for 85 km on a bearing of 067°.
  a How far east has it travelled?
  b How far north has the ship sailed?

2 Rotherham is 11 miles south of Barnsley and 2 miles west of Barnsley.
  What is the bearing of:
  a Barnsley from Rotherham   **b** Rotherham from Barnsley?

3 A plane sets off from airport A and flies due east for 100 km, then turns to fly due south for 80 km before landing at an airport B. What is the bearing of airport B from airport A?

FM **4** Mountain A is due east of a walker. Mountain B is due south of the walker.
  The guidebook says that mountain A is 5 km from mountain B, on a bearing of 038°.
  How far is the walker from mountain B?

5 The diagram shows the relative distances and bearings of three ships A, B and C.
  a How far north of A is B?
    (Distance x on diagram.)
  b How far north of B is C?
    (Distance y on diagram.)
  c How far west of A is C?
    (Distance z on diagram.)
  d What is the bearing of A from C?
    (Angle w on diagram.)

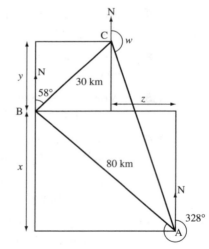

AU **6** An aeroplane is flying from Leeds (L) to London Heathrow (H). It flies 150 miles on a bearing 136° to point A. It then turns through 90° and flies the final 80 miles to H.
  a **i** Show clearly why the angle marked x is equal to 46°.
    ii Give the bearing of H from A.
  b Use Pythagoras' theorem to calculate the distance LH.
  c **i** Calculate the size of the angle marked y.
    ii Work out the bearing of L from H.

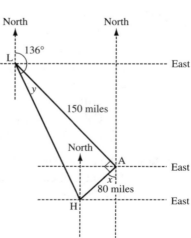

AU 7 A plane flies 200 km on a bearing of 124° and then 150 km on a bearing of 053°.
How far east from its starting point has it travelled?

FM 8 Large boats are supposed to stay at least 300 m from the shore near a particular beach.
Don notices a large boat that is due north from where he is sitting on the beach.
He walks 100 m to the east and uses a compass to find that the bearing of the boat is 340°.
Is the boat breaking the rules?

HOMEWORK 5P

1 Find the side or angle marked x.

a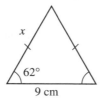

b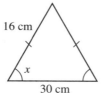

2 This diagram shows a roof truss.
How wide is the roof?

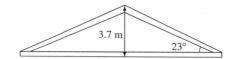

3 Calculate the area of each triangle.

a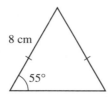

b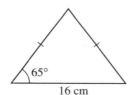

4 An isosceles triangle has two sides of 12 cm and an angle of 62°.
Calculate both possible areas.

AU 5 The largest angle of an isosceles triangle is 152° and the longest side is 60 cm.
Calculate the area of the triangle.

FM 6 Hugo is using roof trusses with the dimensions shown in this diagram.

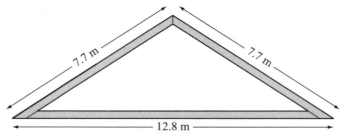

What is the angle of slope of the roof?

Functional Maths Activity
Access ramps

Building regulations in the UK state how steep wheelchair ramps used to access buildings are allowed to be.

Going	Maximum gradient	Maximum rise
10 m	1:20	500 mm
5 m	1:15	333 mm
2 m	1:12	166 mm

Below are some definitions of the jargon used. The diagram that follows illustrates how they are used in practice.

Going: The horizontal length.

Gradient: The tangent of the angle the ramp makes with the horizontal. Here it is written as a ratio.

Rise: The change in height from one end of the ramp to the other.

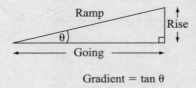

Gradient = tan θ

You can add to the table, using different lengths for the going. Try adding the maximum gradient and maximum rise for goings of 4 m and 9 m, following the number patterns in the table.

A builder has asked you to explain a few things that are puzzling him.

a Is there a connection between the numbers in the three columns?

b What is the difference between the maximum angles for a 2 m going and a 10 m going?

c The builder has been asked to install an access ramp to an old building. The rise required is 400 mm. In order not to exceed the available space, he wants to build a ramp with a 7 m going. Is this permitted, according to the regulations? Explain how you would decide.

Geometry: Angles and properties of circles

6.1 Special triangles and quadrilaterals

HOMEWORK 6A

D

1 For each of these shapes, calculate the value of the lettered angles.

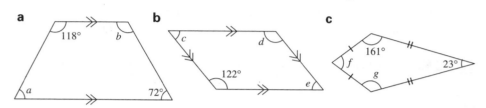

a 118°, b, a, 72°   **b** c, d, 122°, e   **c** 161°, f, g, 23°

2 Calculate the values of x and y in each of these shapes.

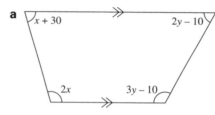 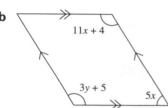

a $x + 30$, $2y - 10$, $2x$, $3y - 10$ **b** $11x + 4$, $3y + 5$, $5x$

PS 3 Find the value of x in each of these quadrilaterals with the following angles and state the type of quadrilateral it is.

  a $x + 10°$, $x + 30°$, $x - 30°$, $x - 50°$ **b** $x°$, $x - 10°$, $3x - 15°$, $3x - 15°$

4 **a** What do the interior angles of a quadrilateral add up to?
    b Use the fact that the angles of a triangle add up to 180°, to prove that the sum of the interior angles of any quadrilateral is 360°.

FM 5 The diagram shows the side wall of a barn.
The architect says that angle D must not be more than twice as big as angle A.
What is the largest possible size of angle D?

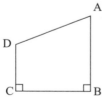

AU 6 The diagram shows a parallelogram ABCD.
AC is a diagonal.
Show that angle x is a right angle.
Give reasons for your answer.

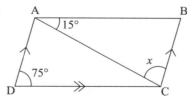

AU 7 Give two reasons to explain why the trapezium is different from the parallelogram.

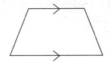 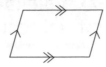

6.2 Angles in polygons

HOMEWORK 6B

 1 Calculate the sum of the interior angles of polygons with:
  a 7 sides **b** 11 sides **c** 20 sides **d** 35 sides

 2 Calculate the size of the interior angle of regular polygons with:
  a 15 sides **b** 18 sides **c** 30 sides **d** 100 sides

 3 Find the number of sides of the polygon with the interior angle sum of:
  a 1440° **b** 2520° **c** 6120° **d** 6840°

4 Find the number of sides of the regular polygon with an exterior angle of:
  a 20° **b** 30° **c** 18° **d** 4°

5 Find the number of sides of the regular polygon with an interior angle of:
  a 135° **b** 165° **c** 170° **d** 156°

 PS 6 What is the name of the regular polygon whose interior angle is three times its exterior angle?

 7 Anne measured all the interior angles in a polygon. She added them up to make 1325°, but she had missed out one angle. What is the:
  a name of the polygon that Anne measured and **b** size of the missing angle?

 AU 8 This shape is made from a regular pentagon and a regular octagon.

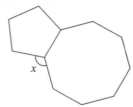

Work out the size of angle x.

 FM 9 Jamal is cutting metal from a rectangular sheet to make this sign.

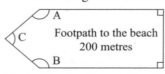

He decides it will look best if angles A and B are the same size and each of them is twice as big as angle C. How big are angles A, B and C?

PS 10 ABCDE is a regular pentagon.

Work out the size of angle ADE.
Give reasons for your answer.

AU 11 Which of the following statements are true for a regular hexagon?
a   The size of each interior angle is 60°
b   The size of each interior angle is 120°
c   The size of each exterior angle is 60°
d   The size of each exterior angle is 240°

6.3 Circle theorems

 HOMEWORK 6C

1   Find the value of x in each of these circles with centre O.

a   b   c

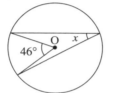   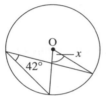   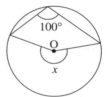

d   e   f

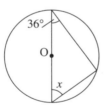   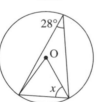   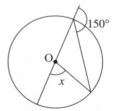

2   Find the value of x in each of these circles.

a   b   c

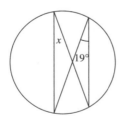   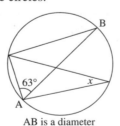   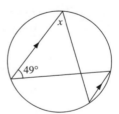

AB is a diameter

3   In the diagram, O is the centre of the circle. Find
a   ∠EDF
b   ∠DEG
c   ∠EGF

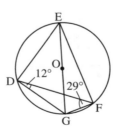

4 Find the values of x and y in each of these circles. O is the centre.

a

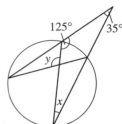

b

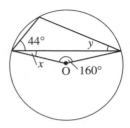

AU 5 In each diagram, O is the centre of a circle.

a Calculate the value of angle a.

b Calculate the value of angle b.

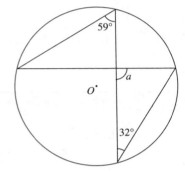

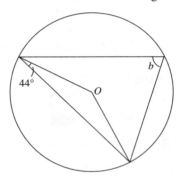

AU 6 On the diagram, O is the centre of the circle.

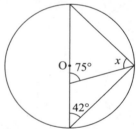

Which of the following is the size of angle x marked on the diagram?

a $48°$ **b** $57°$ **c** $63°$ **d** $75°$

PS 7 On the diagram O is the centre of the circle.

Angle BAC = x and angle CBO = y.

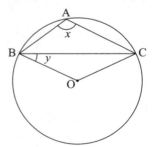

Prove that $y = x - 90°$, giving reasons in your working.

6.4 Cyclic quadrilaterals

HOMEWORK 6D

1 Find the size of the lettered angles in each of these circles.

a
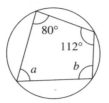

b

c
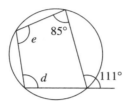

d
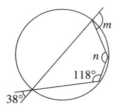

2 Find the values of x and y in each of these circles.

a
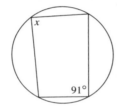

b
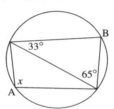

c
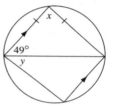

3 Find the values of x and y in each of these circles, centre O.

a
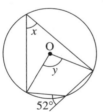

b
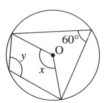

c
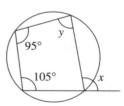

PS 4 ABCD is a cyclic quadrilateral.

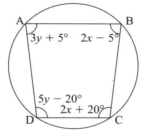

Work out the values of x and y.

AU 5 On the diagram, O is the centre of the circle.
Explain why the angle BOD is 128°.
Give reasons for your answer.

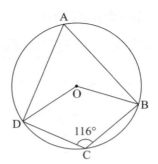

6 ABCD are points on a circle. AB is parallel to CD.
Prove that $x = y$

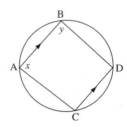

6.5 Tangents and chords

HOMEWORK 6E

1 In each diagram, TP and TQ are tangents to a circle, centre O. Find values for r and x.

a

b

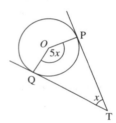

2 Each diagram shows a tangent to a circle, centre O. Find each value of y.

a

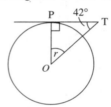

b

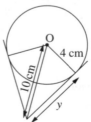

3 Each diagram shows a tangent to a circle, centre O. Find x and y in each case.

a

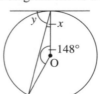

b

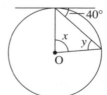

4 In each of the diagrams, TP and TQ are tangents to the circle, centre O. Find each value of x.

a
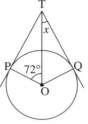

b
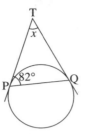

PS 5 The diagram shows two circles touching at X.

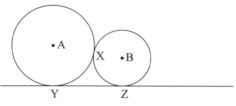

The circles have a common tangent at Y and Z.
The circle with centre A has a radius of 6 cm.
The circle with centre B has a radius of 3 cm.
Calculate the length YZ.

AU 6 Two circles intersect at X and Y.

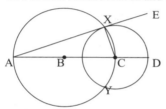

B and C are the centres of the circles and ABCD is a straight line.
Prove that the line AE is a tangent to the small circle.

6.6 Alternate segment theorem

HOMEWORK 6F

1 Find the size of each lettered angle.

a
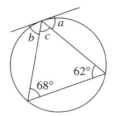

b
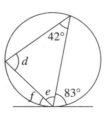

2 In each diagram, find the value of x.

a
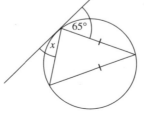

b
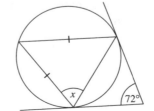

3 In each diagram, find the value of *x* and *y*.

a

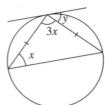

b

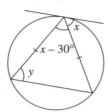

4 ATB is a tangent to the circle, centre O. Find the values of *x*, *y* and *z* in each case.

a

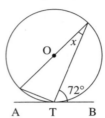

b

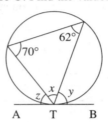

5 O is the centre of the circle. PQT is the tangent to the circle at Q.

Work out the sizes of angles *x*, *y* and *z*.

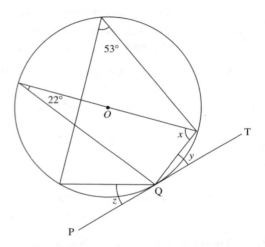

AU 6 On the diagram, O is the centre of the circle.
XY is a tangent to the circle at A.

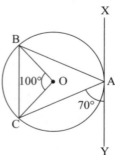

Which of the following is the size of angle OBA?

a 25°   **b** 30°   **c** 35°   **d** 40°

PS 7 AB is a tangent to the circle at X.
YZC is a straight line.

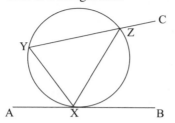

Prove that angle BXY = angle XZC.

Functional Maths Activity

Security cameras

A museum has a circular room which is used to show some of its valuable exhibits.
The room needs to be completely covered by security cameras placed around the wall of the room.
The curator of the museum wants to use as few cameras as possible to keep the cost low and to make the supervision easier.
The curator is thinking of using security cameras with an angle of view of 60°.

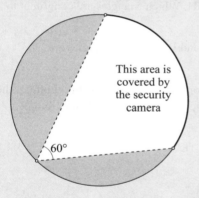

This area is covered by the security camera

60°

1   How many cameras will the curator need for the room?
2   How should the cameras be arranged?

7.1 Congruent triangles

HOMEWORK 7A

1 State whether each pair of triangles below is congruent, giving reasons if they are.

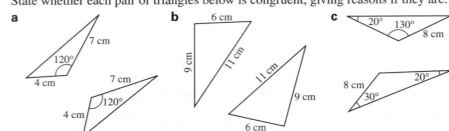

a   7 cm 120° 4 cm 7 cm 120° 4 cm

b   6 cm 9 cm 11 cm 11 cm 9 cm 6 cm

c   20° 130° 8 cm 8 cm 20° 30°

2 Draw a square ABCD. Draw in the diagonals AC and BD. Which triangles are congruent to each other?

3 Draw a kite EFGH. Draw in the diagonals EG and FH. Which triangles are congruent to each other?

4 Draw a rhombus ABCD. Draw in the diagonals AC and BD. Which triangles are congruent to each other?

5 Draw an equilateral triangle ABC. Draw the lines from each vertex to the mid-point of the opposite side. These three lines should all cross at the same point T inside the triangle. Which triangles are congruent to each other?

PS 6 In the diagram, AB and CD are parallel with AB = CD.
The lines AC and BD intersect at X.

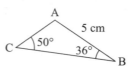

Prove that triangle ABX and triangle CDX are congruent.

AU 7 Helen says that these two triangles are congruent because the three angles are the same.

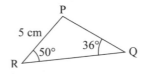

A   5 cm   C 50° 36° B

P   5 cm   R 50° 36° Q

Explain why she is wrong.

7.2 Translations

HOMEWORK 7B

1 Describe these translations with vectors.

i A to B   **ii** A to C   **iii** A to D   **iv** B to A   **v** B to C   **vi** B to D

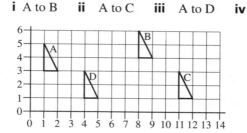

2 a On a grid showing values of x and y from 0 to 10, draw the triangle with coordinates A(4, 4), B(5, 7) and C(6, 5).

   b Draw the image of ABC after a translation with vector $\binom{3}{2}$. Label this P.

   c Draw the image of ABC after a translation with vector $\binom{4}{-3}$. Label this Q.

   d Draw the image of ABC after a translation with vector $\binom{-4}{3}$. Label this R.

   e Draw the image of ABC after a translation with vector $\binom{-3}{-2}$. Label this S.

3 Using your diagram from Question **2**, describe the translation that will move

   a P to Q   **b** Q to R   **c** R to S   **d** S to P

   e R to P   **f** S to Q   **g** R to Q   **h** P to S

FM 4 A group of hikers walk between three points A, B and C using direction vectors with distances in kilometres.

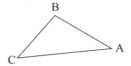

The direction vector from A to B is $\binom{-4}{3}$ and the direction vector from B to C is $\binom{-2}{-5}$.

On centimetre squared paper, draw a diagram to show the walk, using a scale of 1 cm represents 1 km.

Work out the direction vector from C to A.

PS 5 Write down a series of translations which will take you from the Start/finish, around the shaded square without touching it, and back to the Start/finish. Make as few translations as possible.

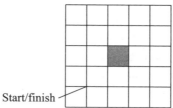

Start/finish

AU 6 Joel says that if the translation from a point X to a point Y is described by the vector $\binom{-3}{2}$, then the translation from the point Y to the point X is described by the vector $\binom{2}{-3}$.

Is Joel correct? Explain how you decide.

7.3 Reflections

HOMEWORK 7C

1
a   Draw a pair of axes with the *x*-axis from –5 to 5 and the *y*-axis from –5 to 5.
b   Draw the triangle with co-ordinates A(1, 1), B(5, 5), C(3, 4).
c   Reflect triangle ABC in the *x*-axis. Label the image P.
d   Reflect triangle P in the *y*-axis. Label the image Q.
e   Reflect triangle Q in the *x*-axis. Label the image R.
f   Describe the reflection that will transform triangle ABC onto triangle R.

AU 2   Copy this diagram onto squared paper.

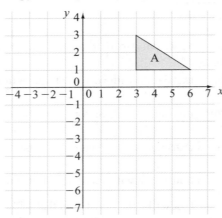

a   Reflect triangle A in the line $x = 1$
    Label the image B.
b   Reflect triangle B in the line $y = -2$
    Label the image C.

FM 3   A designer is making a logo for a company.
She starts with a kite ABCD.
She then reflects the kite in the line BD on top of the
original kite to obtain the logo.
Draw any kite on squared paper to obtain a logo by
following the designer's method.

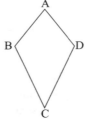

PS 4   A point X has coordinates (a, b).
Point X is reflected in the line $x = 3$
Find the coordinates of the image of point X.

5
a   Draw a pair of axes, *x*-axis from –5 to 5, *y*-axis from –5 to 5.
b   Draw the triangle with co-ordinates A(2, 2), B(3, 4), C(2, 4).
c   Reflect the triangle ABC in the line $y = x$. Label the image P.
d   Reflect the triangle P in the line $y = -x$. Label the image Q.
e   Reflect triangle Q in the line $y = x$. Label the image R.
f   Describe the reflection that will move triangle ABC to triangle R.

7.4 Rotations

HOMEWORK 7D

1 Copy this T-shape on squared paper.

    a Rotate the shape 90° clockwise about the origin 0. Label the image P.

    b Rotate the shape 180° clockwise about the origin 0. Label the image Q.

    c Rotate the shape 90° anticlockwise about the origin 0. Label the image R.

    d What rotation takes R back to the original shape?

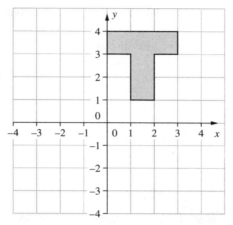

2 Copy this square ABCD on squared paper.

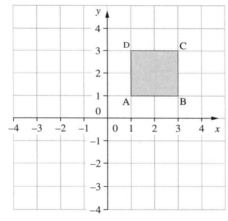

    a Write down the coordinates of the vertices of the square ABCD.

    b Rotate the square ABCD through 90° clockwise about the origin 0. Label the image S. Write down the coordinates of the vertices of the square S.

    c Rotate the square ABCD through 180° clockwise about the origin 0. Label the image T. Write down the coordinates of the vertices of the square T.

    d Rotate the square ABCD through 90° anticlockwise about the origin 0. Label the image U. Write down the coordinates of the vertices of the square U.

    e What do you notice about the coordinates of the four squares?

3 A designer is making a logo for a company.
She starts with a parallelogram ABCD.
She then rotates the parallelogram 90° clockwise about the point of intersection of the two diagonals on top of the original parallelogram to obtain the logo.
Draw any parallelogram on squared paper to obtain a logo by following the designer's method.

4 Copy the diagram and rotate the given triangle by:

a $\frac{1}{4}$ turn clockwise about (0, 0)

b $\frac{1}{2}$ turn clockwise about (0, 2)

c 90° turn anticlockwise about (−1, 1)

d 180° turn about (0, 0).

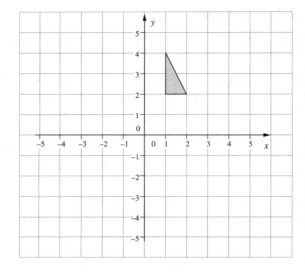

5 Describe the rotation that takes the shaded triangle to:

a triangle A

b triangle B

c triangle C

d triangle D.

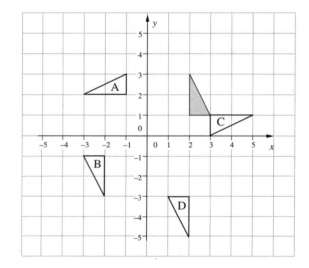

PS 6 A point P has coordinates (a, b).

a The point P is rotated 90° clockwise about (0, 0) to give a point Q. What are the coordinates of Q?

b The point P is rotated 180° clockwise about (0, 0) to give a point R. What are the coordinates of R?

c The point P is rotated 90° anticlockwise about (0, 0) to give a point S. What are the coordinates of S?

AU 7 Triangle A is drawn on a grid.
Triangle A is rotated to form a new triangle B.
The coordinates of B are (3, –1), (1, –4)
and (3, –4).
Describe fully the rotation that maps
triangle A onto triangle B.

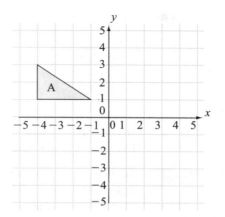

7.5 Enlargements

HOMEWORK 7E

1. Copy each figure below with its centre of enlargement, leaving plenty of space for the enlargement. Then enlarge them by the given scale factor, using the ray method.

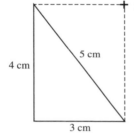

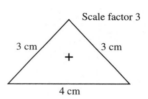

2. Copy each of these diagrams on squared paper and enlarge it by scale factor 2 using the origin as the centre of enlargement.

a
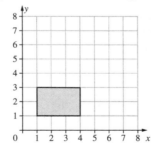

b
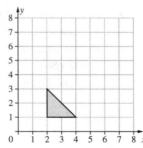

c
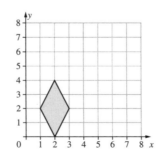

d
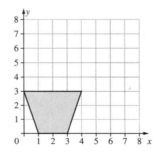

3 Draw a letter T of any size. Now draw another letter T twice the size, as in the diagram.

Use the ray method to find the centre of enlargement.
Draw the rays as dotted lines to create a logo design.

AU 4 Triangle A has coordinates (2, 2), (6, 2) and (6, 4).
Triangle A is enlarged by a scale factor of $\frac{1}{2}$ about the origin to give triangle B.
Find the coordinates of triangle B.

AU 5 Triangle B is an enlargement of triangle A.

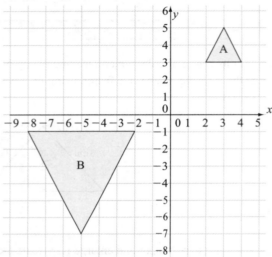

Which of the following describes the enlargement?
a an enlargement of scale factor −2 about (0, 0).
b an enlargement of scale factor −3 about (0, 0).
c an enlargement of scale factor −3 about (1, 2).
d an enlargement of scale factor −$\frac{1}{3}$ about (1, 2).
 Show how you decide.

7.6 Combined transformations

HOMEWORK 7F

1 Describe fully the transformation that will move

a T_1 to T_2 **b** T_1 to T_6 **c** T_2 to T_3 **d** T_6 to T_2

e T_6 to T_5 **f** T_5 to T_4 **g** T_1 to T_5

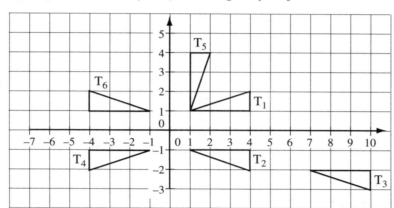

2 **a** Plot a triangle T with vertices (1, 1), (3, 1), (3, 4).
    b Reflect triangle T in the x-axis and label the image T_b.
    c Rotate triangle T_b 90° clockwise about the origin and label the image T_c.
    d Reflect triangle T_c in the x-axis and label the image T_d.
    e Describe fully the transformation that will move triangle T_d back to triangle T.

PS 3 **a** The point P(2, 5) is reflected in the x-axis, then rotated by 90° clockwise about the origin.
    What are the coordinates of the image of P?
    b The point Q(a, b) is reflected in the x-axis, then rotated by 90° clockwise about the origin. What are the coordinates of the image of Q?

PS 4 **a** The point R(4, 3) is reflected in the line $y = -x$, then reflected in the x-axis. What are the coordinates of the image of R?
    b The point S(a, b) is reflected in the line $y = -x$, then reflected in the x-axis. What are the coordinates of the image of S?

AU 5 Copy the diagram onto squared paper.

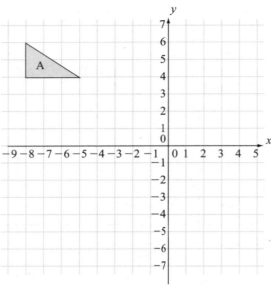

a Triangle A is translated by the vector $\left(\begin{smallmatrix} 9 \\ -3 \end{smallmatrix}\right)$ to give triangle B.
Triangle B is then enlarged by a scale factor –2 about the origin to give triangle C.
Draw triangles B and C on the diagram.

b Describe fully the single transformation that maps triangle C onto triangle A.

Functional Maths Activity

Transformations in the sorting office

When letters are taken to a sorting office they are checked to see if there is a stamp in the top right-hand corner.

Each letter is put through a checking machine and the top right-hand corner is scanned. Of course, the stamp will be detected only if the letter is the right way round.

If no stamp is detected, the letter is rotated automatically and put through the machine again.

Two different rotations are used:

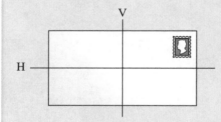

- 180° rotation about the horizontal line H
- 180° rotation about the vertical line V

These rotations will leave the letter in the same orientation, but with the stamp in the other corner.

Functional Maths Activity (continued)

Here is the procedure used:

- Scan the letter.
- If no stamp is detected, rotate about H and scan again.
- If no stamp is detected, rotate about V and scan again.
- If no stamp is detected, rotate about H and scan again.
- If no stamp is detected then the letter is rejected as unstamped.

1 Show that if this procedure is followed then any letter that is correctly stamped will be detected, whichever way the letter is initially fed into the machine.

2 If someone accidentally put the stamp on the top left-hand corner of the letter, would the machine detect it?

3 Suppose that a new regulation requires all letters to be square. Explain why there are now eight corners to be checked for a stamp.

4 With a square letter you could use rotations about either of the diagonals as well as the horizontal and vertical lines. Show how it is still possible to use just two rotations (repeated if necessary) to check all eight corners.

Geometry: Constructions

8.1 Constructing triangles

HOMEWORK 8A

1 Accurately draw each of the following triangles.

a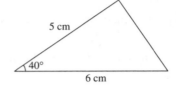

b

c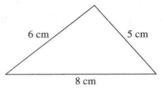

d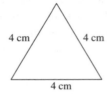

e

2 Draw a triangle ABC with AB = 6 cm, ∠A = 60° and ∠B = 50°.

3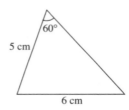

Explain why you can or cannot draw this triangle accurately.

4 **a** Accurately draw the shape on the right.
   b What is the name of the shape you have drawn?

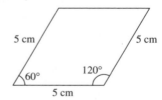

AU 5 Shehab says, "As long as I know two sides of a triangle and the angle between them then I can draw it."
Is Shehab correct?
If not, explain why not.

PS 6 You are asked to construct a triangle with sides 9 cm, 10 cm and an angle of 60°.
Sketch all the possible triangles that you could construct from this description.

FM Functional Maths   **AU** (AO2) Assessing Understanding   **PS** (AO3) Problem Solving

8.2 Bisectors

HOMEWORK 8B

1 Draw a line 8 cm long. Bisect it with a pair of compasses. Check your accuracy by seeing if each half is 4 cm.

2 **a** Draw any triangle.
b On each side construct the line bisector. All your line bisectors should intersect at the same point.
c See if you can use this point as the centre of a circle that fits perfectly inside the triangle.

3 **a** Draw a circle with a radius of about 4 cm.
b Draw a quadrilateral such that the vertices (corners) of the quadrilateral are on the circumference of the circle.
c Bisect two of the sides of the quadrilateral. Your bisectors should meet at the centre of the circle.

4 **a** Draw any angle.
b Construct the angle bisector.
c Check how accurate you have been by measuring each half.

5 The diagram shows a park with two ice-cream sellers A and B. People always go to the ice-cream seller nearest to them. Shade the region of the park from which people go to ice-cream seller B.

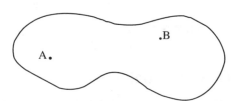

PS 6 Using a straight edge and a pair of compasses only, construct:
a an angle of 15 degrees
b an angle of 75 degrees

AU 7 If I construct all the angle bisectors in a triangle, they will meet at a point.
Explain why I can draw a circle with this as the centre, and this circle will just touch each side of the triangle.

8.3 Defining a locus

HOMEWORK 8C

1 A is a fixed point. Sketch the locus of the point P when AP > 3 cm and AP < 6 cm.

2 A and B are two fixed points 4 cm apart. Sketch the locus of the point P for the following situations:
a AP < BP   **b** P is always within 3 cm of A and within 2 cm of B.

3 A fly is tethered by a length of spider's web that is 1 m long. Describe the locus that the fly can still move around in.

4 ABC is an equilateral triangle of side 4 cm. In each of the following loci, the point P moves only inside the triangle. Sketch the locus in each case.
a AP = BP   **b** AP < BP
c CP < 2 cm   **d** CP > 3 cm and BP > 3 cm

5 A wheel rolls around the inside of a square. Sketch the locus of the centre of the wheel.

6 The same wheel rolls around the outside of the square. Sketch the locus of the centre of the wheel.

7 Two ships A and B, which are 7 km apart, both hear a distress signal from a fishing boat. The fishing boat is less than 4 km from ship A and is less than 4.5 km from ship B.
A helicopter pilot sees that the fishing boat is nearer to ship A than to ship B. Use accurate construction to show the region which contains the fishing boat. Shade this region.

PS 8 On a piece of plain paper, mark three points A, B and C, about 5 to 7 cm away from each other.
Find the locus of point P where:
a P is always closer to a point A than a point B
b P is always equal distances from points B and C

AU 9 Sketch the locus of a point on the rim of a bicycle wheel as it makes three revolutions along a flat road.

8.4 Loci problems

HOMEWORK 8D

For Questions **1** to **3**, you should start by sketching the picture given in each question on a 6 × 6 grid, each square of which is 1 cm by 1 cm. The scale for each question is given.

1 A goat is tethered by a rope, 10 m long, and a stake that is 2 m from each side of a field. What is the locus of the area that the goat can graze? Use a scale of 1 cm : 2 m.

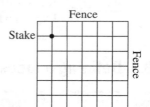

2 A cow is tethered to a rail at the top of a fence 4 m long. The rope is 4 m long. Sketch the area that the cow can graze. Use a scale of 1 cm : 2 m.

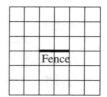

3 A horse is tethered to a corner of a shed, 3 m by 1 m. The rope is 4 m long. Sketch the area that the horse can graze. Use a scale of 1 cm : 1 m.

Tethered here

Shed

For Questions **4** to **7**, you should use a copy of the map on page 72. For each question, trace the map and mark on those points that are relevant to that question.

4 A radio station broadcasts from Birmingham with a range that is just far enough to reach York. Another radio station broadcasts from Glasgow with a range that is just far enough to reach Newcastle.
   a Sketch the area to which each station can broadcast.
   b Will the Birmingham station broadcast as far as Norwich?
   c Will the two stations interfere with each other?

5 An air traffic control centre is to be built in Newcastle. If it has a range of 200 km, will it cover all the area of Britain north of Sheffield and south of Glasgow?

FM 6 A radio transmitter is to be built so that it is the same distance from Exeter, Norwich and Newcastle.
   a Draw the perpendicular bisectors of the lines joining these three places to find where it is to be built.
   b Birmingham has so many radio stations that it cannot have another one within 50 km. Can the transmitter be built?

PS 7 Three radio stations receive a distress call from a boat in the North Sea.
The station at Norwich can tell from the strength of the signal that the boat is within 150 km of the station. The station at Sheffield can tell that the boat is between 100 and 150 km from Sheffield.
If these two reports are correct, then how far away from the helicopter station at Newcastle might the boat be?

AU 8 The locus of a point is described as:
5 cm away from point A
Equidistant from both points A and B
Which of the following could be true?
   a The locus is an arc
   b The locus is just two points
   c The locus is a straight line
   d The locus is none of these

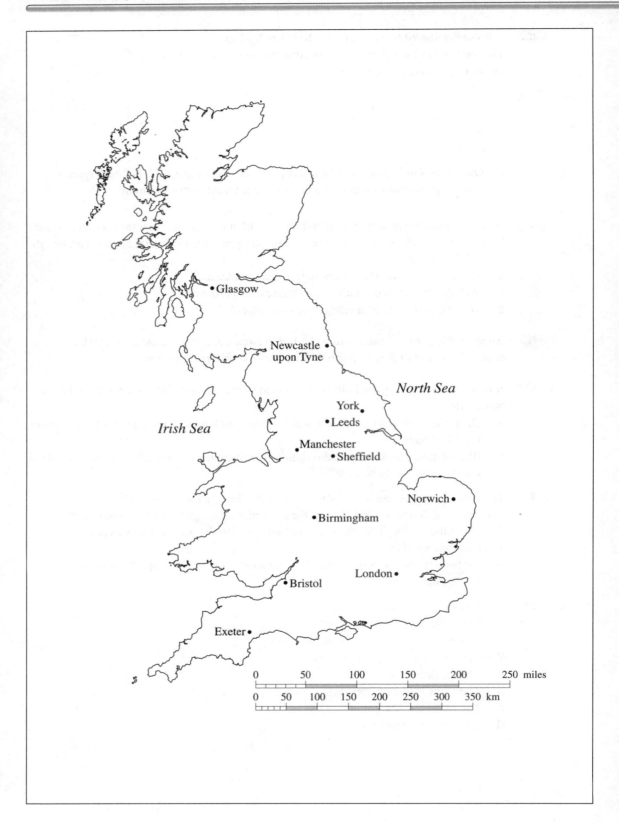

Problem-solving Activity

The nine-point circle

You will have already constructed the circumcircle and circumscribed circle of a triangle. This construction is the nine-point circle of a triangle.

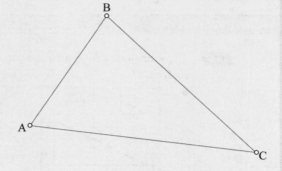

Step 1
Draw a triangle ABC.

Step 2
Construct the mid-points of the three sides and call these L for AB, M for BC and N for AC.

Step 3
Construct the perpendiculars to the opposite sides from the vertices A, B and C. Call the point where they intersect O. Label the feet of the perpendiculars D, E and F on AB, BC and AC respectively.

Step 4
Construct the midpoints of AO, BO and CO. Label these X, Y and Z respectively.

Step 5
Bisect the line segments LM, LN and MN. Call the point where they intersect P.

Step 6
Can you think of a way to check all nine points you have drawn?

9 Measures: Similarity

9.1 Similar triangles

HOMEWORK 9A

1 These diagrams are drawn to scale. What is the scale factor of the enlargement in each case?

a
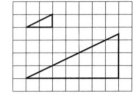

b
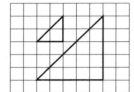

2 **a** Explain why these two shapes are similar.
   b Give the ratio of the sides.
   c Which angle corresponds to angle C?
   d Which side corresponds to side QP?

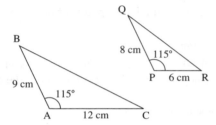

3 In the diagrams below, find the lengths of the sides marked x.
Each pair of shapes is similar but not drawn to scale.

a
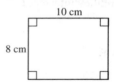

b
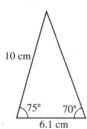
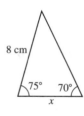

FM 4 Zahid wants to make a frame for his picture. The picture measures 12 cm by 8 cm.

The wood that Zahid is using to make the frame is 10 cm wide.
What length of wood does Zahid need to make the frame, if the picture and the frame are similar.

FM Functional Maths **AU** (AO2) Assessing Understanding **PS** (AO3) Problem Solving

PS 5 Triangle ABC is similar to triangle CDE.

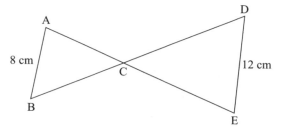

The length of BD is 25 cm.
Work out the lengths of BC and CD.

 AU 6 Triangle ABC is similar to triangle DBE.

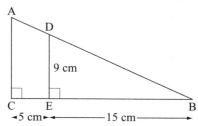

Work out the length of AC.

HOMEWORK 9B

1 In each of the cases below, state a pair of similar triangles and find the length marked x.
Separate the similar triangles if it makes it easier for you.

a 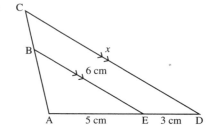 **b**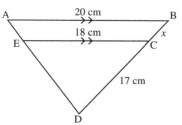

2 In the diagrams below, find the lengths of the sides marked x and y.

a 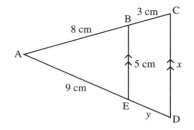 **b**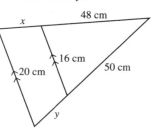

FM 3 Find the height of a lamppost which casts a shadow of 2.1 m when at the same time a
man of height 158 cm casts a shadow of 90 cm.

FM 4 Jamie has designed this metal framework for a garden slide.
Triangles ABC and ADE are similar.

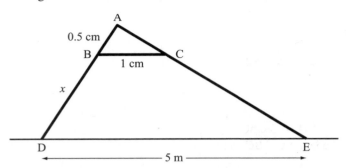

Work out the length of metal he needs for BD, marked x on the diagram.

PS 5 A square ABCD fits inside a triangle DEF.
BE = 10 cm and AE = 6 cm

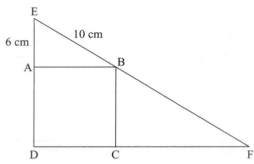

Work out the length of BF.

AU 6 Suzie says that the triangles ABC and CDE are similar.

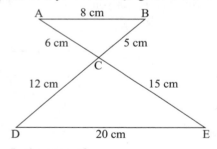

Is she correct?
Show working to explain your answer.

HOMEWORK 9C

1 Find the lengths marked x in the diagrams below.

a

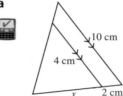

b

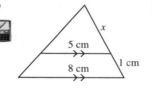

c

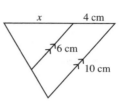

2 Find the lengths x and y in the diagrams below.

a

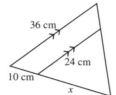

b

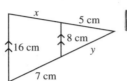

c

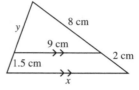

d

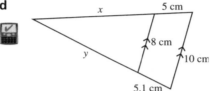

e

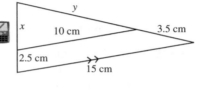

9.2 Areas and volumes of similar shapes

HOMEWORK 9D

1 The length ratio between two similar solids is 3 : 7.
    a What is the area ratio between the solids?
    b What is the volume ratio between the solids?

2 Copy and complete this table.

Linear scale factor	Linear ratio	Linear fraction	Area scale factor	Volume scale factor
4	1 : 4	$\frac{4}{1}$		
$\frac{1}{2}$				
	10 : 1			
			36	
				125

FM 3 Don wants to do some planting in his garden. He marks out a shape with an area of 20 cm². However, he then decides that he wants to use more garden space. What is the area of a similar shape of which the lengths are four times the corresponding lengths of the first shape?

4 A bricklayer uses bricks, each of which has a volume of 400 cm³. He is trying to decide if he should use a different type of brick. What would be the volume of a similar brick, with lengths of:
    a three times the corresponding lengths of the first brick
    b five times the corresponding lengths of the first brick?

A

FM 5 A can of paint, 12 cm high, holds five litres of paint. Help Anita to work out how much paint would go into a similar can that is 30 cm high.

FM 6 A sculptor has made a model statue that is 15 cm high and has a volume of 450 cm^3. The real statue will be 4.5 m high.
In order to buy enough materials, she needs to know the volume of the real statue. Work this out for her, giving your answer in m^3.

FM 7 Tim has a large tin full of paint that he wants to empty into a number of smaller tins. The diagram shows the two sizes of tins.

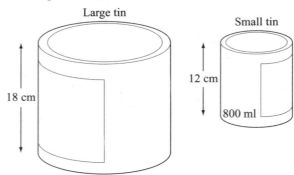

How many small tins can he fill from one large tin?

PS 8 All the lengths of the sides of a cube are increased by 10%.
a What is the percentage increase in the total surface area of the cube?
b What is the percentage increase in the volume of the cube?

AU 9 The length of a standard gift box is 10 cm.
The length of a large gift box is 15 cm.
The large box is similar to the standard box.

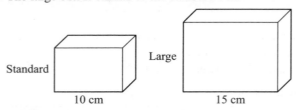

The volume of the standard box is 240 cm^3.
Which of the following is the correct volume of the large box?
a 360 cm^3 **b** 540 cm^3 **c** 720 cm^3 **d** 810 cm^3

HOMEWORK 9E

A*

FM 1 A bottling firm makes similar bottles in three different sizes: small, medium and large. The volumes are:
    i small = 330 cm^3 **ii** medium = 1000 cm^3 **iii** large = 2000 cm^3
a The medium bottle is 20 cm high. Find the heights of the other two bottles.
b The firm designs a label for the large bottle, and wants the labels on the other two bottles to be similar. If the area of the label on the large bottle is 100 cm^2, work out the area of the labels on the other two bottles.

2 It takes 1 kg of grass seed to cover a lawn that is 20 m long. How much seed will be needed to cover a similarly shaped lawn that is 10 m long?

PS **3** Erin's model yacht has a mast that is 40 cm high. She dreams of having a real yacht with a mast that is 4 m high.

    a The sail on her model yacht has an area of 600 cm². What is the area of the sail on the real yacht? Give your answer in m².

    b The real yacht has a hull volume of 20 m³. What is the hull volume of her model yacht? Give your answer in cm³.

4 The ratio of the height of P to the height of Q is 5 : 4. The volume of P is 150 cm³. Calculate the volume of Q.

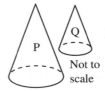

Not to scale

PS **5** Marie has two similar photographs.

       x   28 cm

The areas of the photographs are 200 cm² and 600 cm².
Calculate the length *x* marked on the diagram.

PS **6** These two bottles of cola are similar in shape.

550 ml   850 ml

If the height of one of the bottles is 20 cm, calculate the two possible heights for the other bottle.

AU **7** The surface areas of two spheres are 108 cm² and 300 cm².
The ratio of their volumes is given by which of the following?

    a   3 : 5   **b**   9 : 25   **c**   27 : 125

Functional Maths Activity

Manufacturing dice

Ms Newton runs a company which manufactures small items out of plastic. One item they make is a plastic dice with a side of 2 cm.

Ms Newton wants to make a larger dice. She needs to know what it will cost. This will depend on the amount of plastic required to make it.

1   She thinks that a dice with a side of 4 cm will require twice as much plastic to make as a dice with a side of 2 cm. Explain why this is not the case.
    How much more plastic will be required?

2   She wonders about making a dice with a side of 3 cm. How much more plastic will this use compared to a dice with a side of 2 cm?
    How much less plastic will a dice with a side of 3 cm require, compared to a dice with a side of 4 cm?

3   What advice can you give Ms Newton about the size of a dice that requires twice as much plastic to make one that is 2 cm?

10 Geometry: Trigonometry

10.1 Some 2D problems

HOMEWORK 10A

1 A child's toy consists of a ball that fits into a cone.
The ball has a radius of 3 cm. The base angle of the cone is 38°.
Find:
a AB **b** OB **c** AC

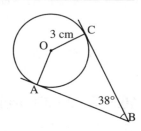

2 From the top of a building 24 m high
the angle of depression of both ends of a
tennis court are 43° and 28° respectively.
a Calculate the length of the court.
b The net is halfway along the court and
is 1 m high. What is the angle of
depression of the top of the net from
the building?

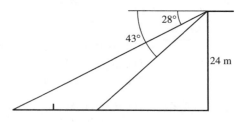

PS 3 A ship leaves point A and travels for 80 km on a bearing of 300° to point B. It then turns
and travels for 40 km on a bearing of 030° to point C. Calculate:
a how far west of A point C is **b** how far north of A point C is
c the bearing of A from C **d** the direct distance of A from C.

FM 4 A tower, CD, is at the top of a hill, BC. Martin is a
surveyor and needs to work out the height of the tower.
He measures the distance AC as 70 m and the angles of
elevation of the top and bottom of the tower as 25° and
42° respectively. Calculate:
a the angle CAD **b** the length AB
c the length CB **d** the height of tower, CD.

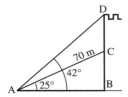

PS 5 Look at this triangle.

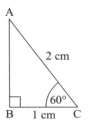

a Use Pythagoras' theorem to work out the length of AB.
Leave your answer in surd form.
b Write down the values of:
i cos 60° **ii** sin 60° **iii** tan 60°
Leave your answers in surd form.

AU **6** In the diagram, triangle ACD is right-angled and triangle ABC is isosceles.

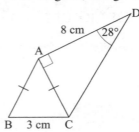

Calculate the size of angle ABC.

PS **7** A regular pentagon is inscribed in a circle of radius 5 cm.
Calculate the length of one of its sides.

10.2 Some 3D problems

HOMEWORK 10B

FM **1** A TV mast XY is 3 km due west of village A.
Village B is 2 km due south of village A.
The angle of elevation from B to the top of the mast is 6°.
Show how a company can use this information to calculate the height of the mast in metres.

2 The diagram shows a pyramid. The base is a
square ABCD, 16 cm by 16 cm. The length of each
sloping edge is 25 cm. The apex, V, is over the centre
of the base. Calculate:

a the size of angle VAC
b the height of the pyramid
c the volume of the pyramid
d the size of the angle between the face VAD
and the base ABCD.

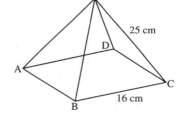

3 In the given cuboid, find:

a angle AGE
b angle BMA.
(M is the midpoint of GH.)

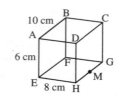

4 The diagram shows a wedge. Find:

a CD
b angle CAD
c angle CAE.
M is the midpoint of AB. Calculate:
d distance DM.

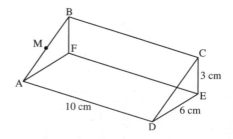

PS 5 A tetrahedron VPQR stands on a prism FGHPQR.
The cross-section PQR is an equilateral triangle of side
8 cm. VP = VQ = VR = 10 cm. PF = QG = RH = 15 cm.
M is the midpoint of QR.

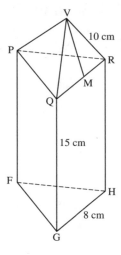

a i Use triangle PQR to find the length of PM.
  ii Use triangle VQR to find the length of VM.
b Find the size of angle VPM.
c Find the height of V above the base FGH. Give your
    answer to an appropriate degree of accuracy.

PS 6 ABCDEF is a triangular prism with edges of lengths a, b and c, as shown
on the diagram below.

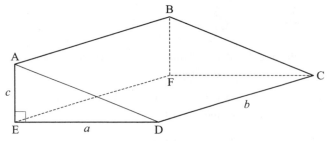

Calculate the angle between BD and DF.

AU 7 XABCD is a right pyramid on a rectangular base.

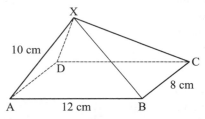

Ben is working out the angle between the edge XA and the base ABCD.
This is his working:
By Pythagoras' theorem
$$AC^2 = 12^2 + 8^2 = 208$$
$$\text{so } AC = \sqrt{208}$$
Let angle XAC = $x°$
$$\cos x = \frac{14.42}{10}$$

$$\text{so } x = \cos^{-1}\frac{14.42}{10}$$

Ben gets an error message on his calculator when he tries to work this out.
Explain where Ben has made the error and write out a correct solution to find
the value of x.

10.3 Solving any triangle

HOMEWORK 10C

1 Find the length x in each of these triangles.

a

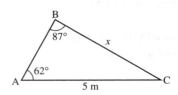

b

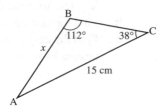

2 Find the angle x in each of these triangles.

a

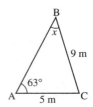

b

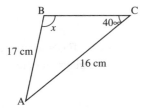

3 In triangle ABC, the angle at A is 40°, the side AB is 10 cm and the side BC is 7 cm. Find the two possible values of the angle at C.

4 In triangle ABC, the angle at A is 58°, the side AB is 20 cm and the side BC is 18 cm. Find the two possible values of the side AC.

FM 5 To calculate the length of a submarine, Mervyn stands on a cliff 60 m high and measures the angle of depression of both ends of the boat. The information is shown in the diagram.

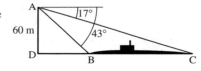

   a Find the value of the angle DAB.
   b Use trigonometry to calculate the length AB.
   c Use the sine rule to work out the length BC.

FM 6 Use the information on this sketch to help the land surveyor calculate the width, w, of the river.

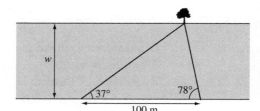

PS FM 7 A surveyor wishes to measure the height of a chimney. Measuring the angle of elevation, she finds that the angle increases from 28° to 37° after walking 30 m towards the chimney. What is the height of the chimney?

PS 8 Ship S and two lighthouses A and B are shown in the diagram below.
A is due west of B and the two lighthouses are 15 km apart.

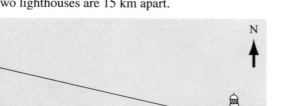

The bearing of the ship from lighthouse A is 330° and the bearing of the ship from lighthouse B is 290°.
How far is the ship from lighthouse B?

9 Triangle ABC has an obtuse angle at A.

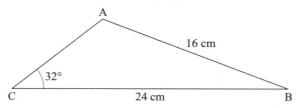

Calculate the size of angle BAC.

HOMEWORK 10D

1 Find the length x in each of these triangles.

a

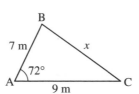

b

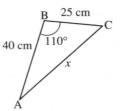

2 Find the angle x in each of these triangles.

a

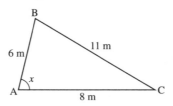

b

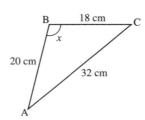

A

FM 3 Harry is travelling on a road which goes directly from X to Y.
The road is closed between A and B because of flooding.
Harry has to make a detour through C.

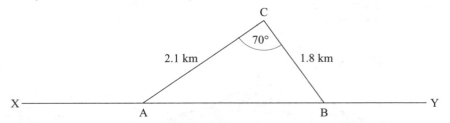

Calculate how much further Harry has to travel by making the detour.

A*

4 A quadrilateral ABCD has AD = 8 cm, DC = 10 cm, AB = 12 cm and BC = 15 cm.
Angle ADC = 112°. Calculate angle ABC.

5 The three sides of a triangle are given as 2*a*, 3*a* and 5*a*.
Calculate the smallest angle in the triangle.

6 The diagram shows a trapezium ABCD.
AB = 6 cm, AD = 8 cm, CB = 12 cm and
angle DAB = 115°. Calculate:

a length DB   **b** angle DBA
c angle DBC   **d** length DC
e area of the trapezium.

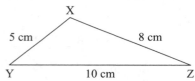

7 A port, B, is 20 km northeast of another port, A.
A lighthouse, L, is 5 km from B on a bearing of 260° from B. Calculate:
a the distance AL   **b** the bearing of L from A to the nearest degree.

PS 8 Work out the size of the smallest angle in the triangle XYZ.

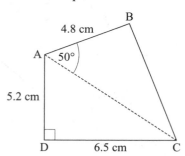

AU 9 ABCD is a quadrilateral. Calculate the perimeter of ABCD.

HOMEWORK 10E

1 Find the length or angle x in each of these triangles.

a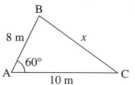

b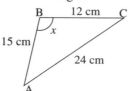

c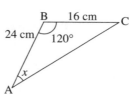

d

e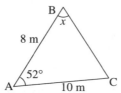

f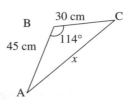

2 The hands of a clock have lengths 10 cm and 7 cm.
Find the distance between the tips of the hands at 5 o'clock.

AU 3 In the quadrilateral ABCD, find:
a angle ABC
b the length of AC.

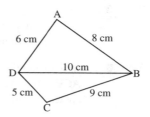

AU 4 In a triangle, ABC, AC = 7.6 cm, angle BAC = 35°, angle ACB = 65°.
The length of AB is x cm. Calculate the value of x.

PS 5 Show that the triangle ABC does not contain an obtuse angle.

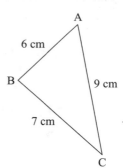

10.4 Trigonometric ratios in surd form

HOMEWORK 10F

AU 1 The sine of angle x is $\frac{3}{4}$.
Work out the cosine of angle x.

AU 2 The cosine of angle x is $\frac{3}{\sqrt{18}}$.
Work out the value of angle x.

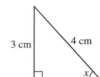

3 Calculate the exact value of the area of an equilateral triangle of side a cm.

4 Work out the exact value of the area of a right-angled isosceles triangle whose hypotenuse is 10 cm.

PS 5 A right-angled triangle has short sides of length $\sqrt{6}$ cm and $\sqrt{10}$ cm.
Show clearly that $(\sin x)^2 + (\cos x)^2 = 1$

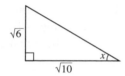

AU 6 In the triangle ABC, AC = 3 cm, BC = 4 cm and angle ACB = 60°. Workout the length of AB, giving your answer in surd form.

10.5 Using sine to find the area of a triangle

HOMEWORK 10G

1 Find the area of each of the following triangles.
   a Triangle ABC where BC = 8 cm, AC = 10 cm and angle ACB = 69°.
   b Triangle ABC where angle BAC = 112°, AC = 3 cm and AB = 7 cm.

2 The area of triangle ABC is 27 cm². If BC = 12 cm and angle BCA = 98°, find AC.

3 In a quadrilateral ABCD, DC = 3 cm, BD = 8 cm, angle BAD = 43°, angle ABD = 52° and angle BDC = 72°. Calculate the area of the quadrilateral.

4 The area of triangle LMN is 85 cm², LM = 10 cm and MN = 25 cm. Calculate:
   a angle LMN   **b** angle MNL.

5 A signwriter wants to use a triangular shaped board with sides 30 cm, 40 cm and 60 cm. Help him to find its area.

AU 6 In the triangle ABC, angle B is **obtuse**, ∠BAC = 32°, AC = 10 cm, BC = 6 cm. Calculate the area of the triangle ABC.

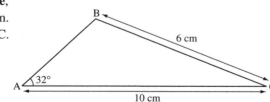

FM 7 The diagram shows a sketch of the shape of a farmer's orchard.

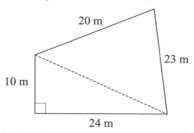

a Help the farmer to calculate the area of the orchard.
Give your answer to an appropriate degree of accuracy.

b For each 5 m² the farmer will plant a tree. How many trees can he plant in the orchard?

PS 8 ABCD is a parallelogram.
AB = a and BC = b.
Angle ABC = θ.

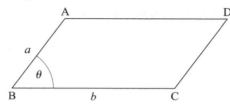

Prove that the area, A, of the parallelogram is given by the formula:
$A = ab \sin \theta$.

AU 9 ABCD is a quadrilateral.

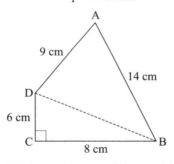

Work out the area of the quadrilateral.
Give your answer to an appropriate degree of accuracy.

Problem-solving Activity

Trigonometry and shapes

A formula for the area of a triangle with sides a, b and c is:

$$\text{Area} = \sqrt{s(s-a)(s-b)(s-c)}$$

where $s = \frac{1}{2}(a + b + c)$

1   Use this formula to find the area of a right-angled triangle with integer sides and show that it gives the correct answer.

2   Use the formula to find the area of an equilateral triangle. Find the area of this triangle by a different method and show that the formula gives the correct answer.

3   A piece of land is roughly triangular in shape. The sides of the triangle are 18 metres, 22 metres and 24 metres.
What is the area of the piece of land?

4   A field is a quadrilateral in shape. You have been asked to find the area of the field. You have a long measuring tape to help you.
What measurements would you take and how would you use them to find the area of the field?

Algebra: More graphs and equations

11.1 Quadratic graphs

1 **a** Copy and complete the table or use a calculator to work out values for the graph of $y = 2x^2$ for $-3 \leqslant x \leqslant 3$.

x	-3	-2	-1	0	1	2	3
$y = 2x^2$	18		2			8	

  b Use your graph to find the value of y when $x = -1.4$.

  c Use your graph to find the values of x that give a y-value of 10.

2 **a** Copy and complete the table or use a calculator to work out values for the graph of $y = x^2 + 3$ for $-5 \leqslant x \leqslant 5$.

x	-5	-4	-3	-2	-1	0	1	2	3	4	5
$y = x^2 + 3$	28		12					7			28

  b Use your graph to find the value of y when $x = 2.5$.

  c Use your graph to find the values of x that give a y-value of 10.

3 **a** Copy and complete the table or use a calculator to work out values for the graph of $y = x^2 - 3x + 2$ for $-3 \leqslant x \leqslant 4$.

x	-3	-2	-1	0	1	2	3	4
$y = x^2 - 3x + 2$	20			2			2	

  b Use your graph to find the value of y when $x = -1.5$.

  c Use your graph to find the values of x that give a y-value of 2.5.

PS 4 Tom is drawing quadratic equations of the form $y = x^2 + bx + c$.
He notices that two of his graphs pass through the point (2, 5).
Which of the following equations are those of the two graphs?

  Equation A: $y = x^2 + 3$

  Equation B: $y = x^2 + 1$

  Equation C: $y = x^2 + 2x - 3$

  Equation D: $y = x^2 - x + 5$

11.2 The significant points of a quadratic graph

1 **a** Copy and complete the table to draw the graph of $y = x^2 - 5x + 4$ for $-1 \leqslant x \leqslant 6$

x	-1	0	1	2	3	4	5	6
$y = x^2 - 5x + 4$	10	4				0		

  b Use your graph to find the roots of the equation $x^2 - 5x + 4 = 0$

2 **a** Copy and complete the table to draw the graph of $y = x^2 - 3x + 2$ for $-1 \leqslant x \leqslant 5$

x	-1	0	1	2	3	4	5
$y = x^2 - 3x + 2$	6	2			1		

b Use your graph to find the roots of the equation $x^2 - 3x + 2 = 0$

3 **a** Copy and complete the table to draw the graph of $y = x^2 + 4x - 6$ for $-5 \leqslant x \leqslant 2$

x	-5	-4	-3	-2	-1	0	1	2
$y = x^2 + 4x - 6$	-1							6

b Use your graph to find the roots of the equation $x^2 + 4x - 6 = 0$

4 Using your answers to question **1**, write down:
a the coordinates of the point where the graph crosses the y-axis
b the coordinates of the minimum point of the graph.

5 Using your answers to question **2**, write down:
a the coordinates of the point where the graph crosses the y-axis
b the coordinates of the minimum point of the graph.

PS 6 Using your answers to question **3** to complete these questions.
a Write down the coordinates of the minimum point of the graph.
b Write the equation $x^2 + 4x - 6 = 0$ in the form $(x - a)^2 + b = 0$
c What is the connection between minimum point and the values in the equation when it is written as $(x - a)^2 + b$
d Without drawing the curve, predict the minimum point of the graph $y = x^2 + 6x - 5$

AU 7 Beryl draws a quadratic graph which has a minimum point at $(2, -6)$.
She forgets to label it and later cannot remember what the quadratic function was.
She knows it is of the form $y = x^2 + px + q$.
Can you help her?

11.3 Other graphs

HOMEWORK 11C

1 **a** Complete the table to draw the graph of $y = x^3 + 1$ for $-3 \leqslant x \leqslant 3$

x	-3	-2	-1	0	1	2	3
$y = x^3 + 1$	-26			1			28

b Use your graph to find the y-value for an x-value of 1.2.

2 **a** Complete the table to draw the graph of $y = x^3 + 2x$ for $-2 \leqslant x \leqslant 3$

x	-2	-1	0	1	2	3
$y = x^3 + 2x$	-12		0		12	

b Use your graph to find the y-value for an x-value of 2.5.

3 **a** Complete the table to draw the graph of $y = \dfrac{12}{x}$ for $-12 \leqslant x \leqslant 12$

x	-12	-6	-4	-3	-2	-1	1	2	3	4	6	12
$y = \dfrac{12}{x}$	-1			-4					4			1

b Use your graph to find:
i the y-value when $x = 1.5$ **ii** the x-value when $y = 5.5$.

4 **a** Complete the table to draw the graph of $y = \dfrac{50}{x}$ for $0 \leqslant x \leqslant 50$

x	1	2	5	10	25	50
$y = \dfrac{50}{x}$						

b On the same axes, draw the line $y = x + 30$
c Use your graph to find the x-value of the point where the graphs cross.

5 **a** Complete the table below for $y = 2^x$ for values of x from -3 to $+4$. (Values are rounded to 2 dp.)

x	-3	-2	-1	0	1	2	3	4
$y = 2^x$	0.1	0.3			2	4		

b Plot the graph of $y = 2^x$ for $-3 \leqslant x \leqslant 4$ (Take y-axis from 0 to 20)
c Use your graph to estimate the value of y when $x = 2.5$
d Use your graph to estimate the value of x when $y = 0.75$

PS 6 Granny has two nephews, Alf and Bert. She writes a will leaving Alf £1000 in the first year after her death, £2000 in the second year after her death, £3000 the next year and so on for 20 years. She leaves Bert £1 the first year, £2 the second year, £4 the next year and so on.
a Show that the formula $500n(n + 1)$ gives the total amount that Alf gets after n years.
b Show that the formula $2^n - 1$ gives the total amount that Bert gets after n years.
c Complete the table for the total amount of money that Bert gets.

Year	2	4	6	8	10	12	14	16	18	20
Total	3	15	63							

d Draw a graph of both nephews' total over 20 years. Take the x-axis from 0 to 20 years and the y-axis from £0 to £110 000.
e Which nephew gets the better deal?

AU 7 A curve of the form $y = ab^x$ passes through the points $(0, 3)$ and $(2, 48)$.
Work out the values of a and b.

11.4 Trigonometric ratios of angles between 90° and 360°

HOMEWORK 11D

1 State the two angles between 0° and 360° for each of these sine values.
a 0.4 **b** 0.45 **c** 0.65 **d** 0.27
e 0.453 **f** -0.4 **g** -0.15 **h** -0.52

PS 2 Solve the equation $2 \sin x = 1$ for $0° \leqslant x \leqslant 360°$.

3   sin 40° = 0.643. Write down the sine values of these angles.

     i 140°   **ii** 320°   **iii** 400°   **iv** 580°

PS 4   Solve the equation $3 \sin x = -2$ for $0° \leqslant x \leqslant 360°$.

AU 5   Which of these ratios is the odd one out and why?

     sin 36°   sin 78°   sin 119°   sin 320°

HOMEWORK 11E

1   State the two angles between 0° and 360° for each of these cosine values.

     a 0.7   **b** 0.38   **c** 0.617   **d** 0.376

     e 0.085   **f** −0.6   **g** −0.45   **h** −0.223

PS 2   Solve the equation $3 \cos x = -1$ for $0° \leqslant x \leqslant 360°$.

3   cos 50° = 0.643. Write down the cosine values of these angles.

     i 130°   **ii** 310°   **iii** 410°   **iv** 590°

PS 4   Solve the equation $6 \cos x = -1$ for $0° \leqslant x \leqslant 360°$.

AU 5   Which of these ratios is the odd one out and why?

     cos 68°   cos 112°   cos 248°   cos 338°

HOMEWORK 11F

1   Write down the sine of each of these angles.

     a 27°   **b** 153°   **c** 207°   **d** 333°

2   Write down the cosine of each of these angles.

     a 69°   **b** 111°   **c** 249°   **d** 291°

3   What do you notice about the answers to Questions **1** and **2**?

AU 4   Find four values between 0° and 360° such that:

     a $\sin x = \pm 0.4$ **b** $\cos x = \pm 0.5$

PS 5   Solve: **a** $\sin x + 1 = 2$ for $0° \leqslant x \leqslant 360°$ **b** $2 + 3 \cos x = 1$ for $0° \leqslant x \leqslant 360°$

PS 6   Find two values of x between 0° and 360° such that $\sin x = \cos 320°$.

HOMEWORK 11G

1   State the angles between 0° and 360° for each of these tangent values.

     a 0.528   **b** 0.8   **c** 1.35   **d** 3.24

     e −2.55   **f** −0.158   **g** −0.786   **h** −1.999

AU 2   tan 64° = 2.05. Write down the tangent values of these angles.

     i 116°   **ii** 296°   **iii** 424°   **iv** 604°

11.5 The circular function of graphs

HOMEWORK 11H

1 Given that $\sin 55° = 0.819$, find another angle between 0° and 360° that also has a sine of 0.819.

2 Given that $\sin 225° = -0.707$, find another angle between 0° and 360° that also has a sine of –0.707.

3 Given that $\cos 27° = 0.891$, find another angle between 0° and 360° that also has a cosine of 0.891.

4 Given that $\cos 123° = -0.545$, find another angle between 0° and 360° that also has a cosine of –0.545.

5 Given that $\sin 60° = 0.866$, find two angles between 0° and 360° that have a sine of –0.866.

6 Given that $\cos 30° = 0.866$, find two angles between 0° and 360° that have a cosine of –0.866.

7 Given that $\cos 38° = 0.788$:
 a write down an angle between 0° and 360° that has a sine of 0.788
 b find two angles between 0° and 360° that have a cosine of –0.788
 c find two angles between 0° and 360° that have a sine of –0.788.

PS 8 **a** Choose an obtuse angle a. Write down the values of:
  i $\sin a$ **ii** $\sin (180° - a)$
 b Repeat with another acute angle b.
 c Write down a rule connecting the sine of an obtuse angle x and the sine of the supplementary angle (i.e. the difference with 180°).
 d Find a similar rule for the cosine of x and the cosine of its supplementary angle.

AU 9 A formula used to work out the angle of a triangle is $\cos A \dfrac{b^2 + c^2 - a^2}{2bc}$, where a, b and c
 are the sides of the triangle and angle A is the angle opposite side a.
 Bill uses the formula to work out the angle A in this triangle, where $a = 18$, $b = 7$ and $c = 8$.

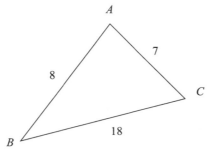

 a Work out the value of cos A for these values.
 b Explain why Bill cannot find a value for A.

11.6 Solving equations, one linear and one non-linear, with graphs

HOMEWORK 11I

Find the approximate or exact solutions to the following pairs of simultaneous equations using graphical methods.

The sizes of the axes needed are given in brackets.

1 $y = x^2 + 5x - 3$ and $y = x$ $(-10 \leqslant x \leqslant 5, -10 \leqslant y \leqslant 5)$

2 $x^2 + y^2 = 25$ and $x + y = 2$ $(-6 \leqslant x \leqslant 6, -6 \leqslant y \leqslant 6)$

3 $y = x^2 - 3x + 2$ and $y = x + 2$ $(-5 \leqslant x \leqslant 5, -5 \leqslant y \leqslant 5)$

4 $y = x^2 - 5$ and $y = x + 3$ $(-5 \leqslant x \leqslant 5, -6 \leqslant y \leqslant 10)$

PS 5
   a $y = x^2 + 2x - 1$ and $y = 4x - 2$ $(-5 \leqslant x \leqslant 5, -5 \leqslant y \leqslant 10)$
   b What is special about the intersection of these two graphs?
   c Show that $4x - 2 = x^2 + 2x - 1$ can be rearranged to: $x^2 - 2x + 1 = 0$
   d Factorise and solve: $x^2 - 2x + 1 = 0$
   e Explain how the solution in **d** relates to the intersection of the graphs.

AU 6
   a $y = x^2 + 3x + 5$ and $y = 2x - 1$ $(-5 \leqslant x \leqslant 5, -5 \leqslant y \leqslant 8)$
   b What is special about the intersection of these two graphs?
   c Rearrange $2x - 1 = x^2 + 3x + 5$ into the general quadratic form:
      $ax^2 + bx + c = 0$
   d Work out the discriminant $b^2 - 4ac$ for the quadratic in **c**.
   e Explain how the value of the discriminant relates to the intersection of the graphs.

11.7 Solving equations by the method of intersection

HOMEWORK 11J

1 Below is the graph of: $y = x^2 - 2x - 4$

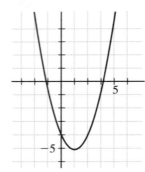

Use this graph to solve:
a $x^2 - 2x - 4 = 0$
b $x^2 - 2x - 4 = 4$
c $x^2 - 2x - 3 = 0$

PS **2** Below are the graphs of: $y = x^2 - 3x + 1$, $y = x - 1$ and $y + x = 2$

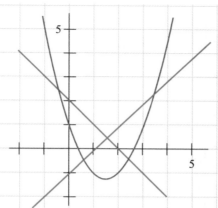

Use these graphs to solve:

a $x^2 - 3x + 1 = 0$
b $2x - 3 = 0$
c $x^2 - 3x - 1 = 0$
d $x^2 - 4x + 2 = 0$
e $x^2 - 2x - 1 = 0$

3 Draw the graph of: $y = x^3 - 2x + 3$
a Use the graph to solve: **i** $x^3 - 2x + 3 = 0$ **ii** $x^3 - 2x = 0$
b Draw a straight-line graph to solve: $x^3 - 3x + 2 = 0$
Draw this line and solve: $x^3 - 3x + 2 = 0$

4 The graph of $y = x^3 - 4x - 1$ is shown on the right.
a Use the graph to solve:
  i $x^3 - 4x - 1 = 0$
  ii $x^3 - 4x + 2 = 0$
b By drawing an appropriate straight line, solve the equation: $x^3 - 5x - 1 = 0$

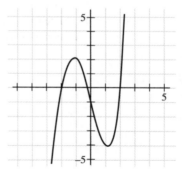

5 The graph of $y = x^3 - 4x$ is shown.
a Use the graph to find the two positive solutions to:
$x^3 - 4x = -2$
b By drawing an appropriate straight line, use the graph to solve: $x^3 - 3x + 1 = 0$

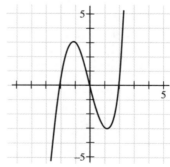

A*

PS **6** The graph shows the lines A: $y = x^2 + 5x - 3$; B: $y = x$; C: $y = x + 3$; D: $y + x = 2$ and
E: $y = -x$

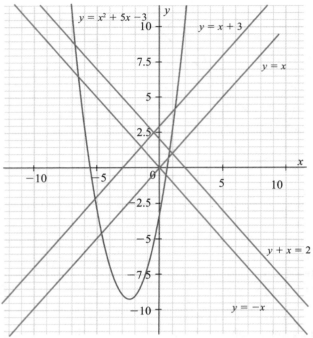

a Which pair of lines has a common solution of (−1.5, 1.5)?

b Which pair of lines has the approximate solutions (1, 1) and (−6.8, 8.8)?

c What quadratic equation has an approximate solution of (−5.2, −2.2) and (1.2, 4.2)?

d The minimum point of the graph $y = x^2 + 5x - 3$ is at (−2.5, −9.25).
Write down the minimum point of the graph: $y = x^2 + 5x - 8$

Problem-solving Activity

Quadratic graphs

The sketch below shows the graphs of $y = x^2$ and $y = x^2 + 3x$.

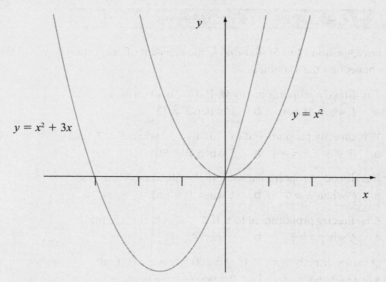

Use a graphical calculator or graphing software on a computer to draw the graphs of $y = x^2$ and $y = x^2 + 3x$ on the same axes.

Now draw the graphs of $y = x^2 + 4x$, $y = x^2 - 2x$ and $y = x^2 - x$ on the same axes.

Describe anything that you notice about these graphs.

What effect does adding or subtracting a term in x have on the graph of $y = x^2$?

Where do these graphs cross the x-axis?

12 Number: Variation

12.1 Direct variation

HOMEWORK 12A

For Questions **1** to **5**, first find k, the constant of proportionality, and then the formula connecting the variables.

1 T is directly proportional to M. If $T = 30$ when $M = 5$, find:
  a T when $M = 4$ **b** M when $T = 75$

2 W is directly proportional to F. If $W = 54$ when $F = 3$, find:
  a W when $F = 4$ **b** F when $W = 90$

3 P is directly proportional to A. If $P = 50$ when $A = 2$; find:
  a P when $A = 5$ **b** A when $P = 150$

4 A is directly proportional to t. If $A = 45$ when $t = 5$, find:
  a A when $t = 8$ **b** t when $A = 18$

5 Q varies directly with P. If $Q = 200$ when $P = 5$, find:
  a Q when $P = 3$ **b** P when $Q = 300$

FM 6 The distance covered by a train is directly proportional to the time taken.
The train travels 135 miles in 3 hours.
  a What distance will the train cover in 4 hours?
  b What time will it take for the train to cover 315 miles?

FM 7 The cost of petrol is directly proportional to the amount put in the tank.
When 40 litres is used, it costs £32.00. How much:
  a will it cost for 30 litres?
  b petrol would there be if the cost were £38.40?
  c A tank holds 60 litres when full. Petrol is put into the tank until it is full.
    The petrol costs £25.
    How much petrol was in the tank before it was filled up?

FM 8 The number of people who can meet safely in a room is directly proportional to the area of the room. A room with an area of 200 m² is safe for 50 people.
  a How many people can safely meet in a room of area 152 m²?
  b A committee has 24 members. What is the smallest room area in which they could safely meet?
  c An extension is to be built on to a room which is safe for 50 people so that it can accommodate another 20 people.
    The cost of extending is estimated at £160 per square metre.
    How much is the estimate for the extension?

AU 9 A man lays 36 paving stones in 3 hours.
  a Working at the same rate, how long would he take to lay 45 paving stones?
  b He works for 7 hours each day. He has 320 stones to lay.
    He employs another worker who can lay 10 stones each hour.
    Will they be able to complete the work in 2 days?

FM Functional Maths **AU** (AO2) Assessing Understanding **PS** (AO3) Problem Solving

HOMEWORK 12B

For Questions **1** to **5**, first find k, the constant of proportionality, and then the formula connecting the variables.

1 T is directly proportional to x^2. If $T = 40$ when $x = 2$, find:
     a T when $x = 5$ **b** x when $T = 400$

2 W is directly proportional to M^2. If $W = 10$ when $M = 5$, find:
     a W when $M = 4$ **b** M when $W = 64$

3 A is directly proportional to r^2. If $A = 96$ when $r = 4$, find:
     a A when $r = 5$ **b** r when $A = 12$

4 E varies directly with $\sqrt{C}$. If $E = 60$ when $C = 36$, find:
     a E when $C = 49$ **b** C when $E = 160$

5 X is directly proportional to $\sqrt{Y}$. If $X = 80$ when $Y = 16$, find:
     a X when $Y = 100$ **b** Y when $X = 48$

FM 6   The distance covered by a train is directly proportional to the time taken.
The train travels 144 miles in 4 hours.
     a   What distance will the train cover in 2 hours 30 minutes?
     b   What time will it take for the train to cover 54 miles?

FM 7   The cost of petrol is directly proportional to the amount put in the tank.
When 40 litres is used, it costs £44.00. How much:
     a   will it cost for 18 litres   **b**   petrol would there be if the cost were £27.50?

8 y is directly proportional to $\sqrt[3]{x}$.
If $y = 4$ when $x = 8$, find the following:
     a y when $x = 1$
     b x when $y = 250$

FM 9   The number of people who can meet safely in a room is directly proportional to the area of the room. A room with an area of 200 m^2 is safe for 50 people.
     a   How many people can safely meet in a room of area 168 m^2?
     b   A committee has 36 members. What is the smallest room area in which they could safely meet?

10   A man lays 36 paving stones in 3 hours.
Working at the same rate how long would he take to lay 54 paving stones?

FM 11   An artist is painting pictures.
The amount of time taken to complete a picture is directly proportional to the square of the width of the picture.
     A picture is 30 cm wide and takes 20 hours to complete.
     A buyer wants a picture that is 50 cm wide within 10 days.
     If the artist paints for 6 hours each day, can he complete the picture on time?

A

PS AU **12** Here are three proportion statements and two tables.

a $y \propto x^2$ **b** $y \propto x$ **c** $y \propto \sqrt{x}$

A

x	1	4	9
y	2	4	6

B

x	1	2	3
y	4	8	12

Match each table to the correct proportion statement.

12.2 Inverse variation

HOMEWORK 12C

For Questions **1** to **7**, first find the formula connecting the variables.

1 T is inversely proportional to m. If $T = 7$ when $m = 4$, find:
   a T when $m = 5$ **b** m when $T = 56$

2 W is inversely proportional to x. If $W = 6$ when $x = 15$, find:
   a W when $x = 3$ **b** x when $W = 10$

3 M varies inversely with t^2. If $M = 10$ when $t = 2$, find:
   a M when $t = 4$ **b** t when $M = 160$

4 C is inversely proportional to f^2. If $C = 20$ when $f = 3$, find:
   a C when $f = 5$ **b** f when $C = 720$

5 W is inversely proportional to $\sqrt{T}$. If $W = 8$ when $T = 36$, find:
   a W when $T = 25$ **b** T when $W = 0.75$

6 H varies inversely with $\sqrt{g}$. If $H = 20$ when $g = 16$, find:
   a H when $g = 1.25$ **b** g when $H = 40$

7 y is inversely proportional to the cube of x. If $y = 10$ when $x = 1$, find the following:
   a y when $x = 2$
   b x when $y = 270$

FM **8** The brightness of a bulb decreases inversely with the square of the distance away from the bulb. The brightness is 5 candle power at a distance of 10 m.
What is the brightness at a distance of 5 m?

AU **9** In the table, y is inversely proportional to x.

x	2	4	16
y	8		

Copy and complete the table.

10 The density of a series of spheres with the same weight is inversely proportional to the cube of the radius. A sphere with a density of 10 g/cm^3 has a radius of 5 cm.
   a What would be the density of a sphere with a radius of 10 cm?
   b If the density was 80 g/cm^3 what would the radius of the sphere be?

11 Given that y is inversely proportional to the square of x, and that y is 12 when $x = 4$:
   a find an expression for y in terms of x.
   b Calculate: **i** y when $x = 6$ **ii** x when $y = 36$

FM 12 The time taken to build an extension is inversely proportional to the number of workers. It takes 2 workers 7 days to complete an extension.

a Three workers start an extension on Monday morning.
Will they complete it by Friday?
Show your working.

b Give a reason why the time taken might not be inversely proportional to the number of workers when the number of workers is very large.

Functional Maths Activity

Taxi fares

Imagine you run a taxi company.

A rival taxi company has a fares structure based on three things:

- a minimum fare of £2.50
- a charge for the time taken
- a charge for the distance travelled.

The charge for the time taken is directly proportional to the time taken.

The charge for the distance travelled is directly proportional to the distance travelled.

You have collected this information about the rival company's fares.

Use this information to work out the charge per mile and the charge per minute, then suggest a competitive pricing structure for your own taxi firm.

Time taken	2 minutes	5 minutes	10 minutes	12 minutes	15 minutes
Distance	1 mile	2 miles	3 miles	5 miles	6 miles
Total charge	£2.50 (minimum fare)	£4.00	£6.50	£9.90	£12.00

13 Geometry: Vectors

13.1 Properties of vectors

HOMEWORK 13A

1 Vectors **a**, **b** and **c** are shown on the diagram.

    a Draw the vectors represented by:

        i **a** + **b**   **ii** −**a**   **iii** **a** − **b**

        iv **b** − **a**   **v** −**b**   **vi** −**a** − **b**

    b Explain the connection between the answers to parts **i** and **vi** and parts **iii** and **iv**.

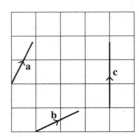

2 The diagram shows vectors **a**, **b** and **c**.

    a Draw the vectors shown by: **i** **a** + **b**   **ii** **a** + **b** + **c**

    b Explain the answer to **a** part **ii**.

    c Write the vectors **a**, **b** and **c** as column vectors.

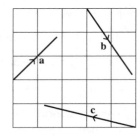

3 The diagram shows three vectors **a**, **b** and **c**.

    a is $\overrightarrow{OA}$, **b** is $\overrightarrow{OB}$ and **c** is $\overrightarrow{OC}$.

    a is the vector $\binom{2}{2}$ **b** is the vector $\binom{4}{1}$

    c is the vector $\binom{6}{0}$

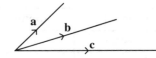

    a Write as a column vector and show on a diagram the vectors:

        i $\overrightarrow{AB}$ **ii** $\overrightarrow{AC}$ **iii** $\overrightarrow{BC}$

    b What do your answers to **a** tell you?

    c Would parts **i** and **ii** of **a** be enough to tell you that ABC is a straight line? Explain your answer.

4 $\overrightarrow{OA}$ and $\overrightarrow{OB}$ are vectors **a** and **b**. M is the midpoint of AB.

    a Express in terms of **a** and **b** the vectors:

        i $\overrightarrow{AB}$ **ii** $\overrightarrow{AM}$ **iii** $\overrightarrow{OM}$

    b Draw on a copy of the diagram, the points X and Y such that: $\overrightarrow{OX} = 2\mathbf{a} + \mathbf{b}$ and $\overrightarrow{OY} = \mathbf{a} + 2\mathbf{b}$

    Express $\overrightarrow{XY}$ in terms of **a** and **b**.

    c What other vector on the diagram is equivalent to $\overrightarrow{XY}$?

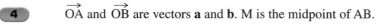

   FM Functional Maths   **AU** (AO2) Assessing Understanding   **PS** (AO3) Problem Solving

5 OACB is a trapezium, where $\overrightarrow{OA}$ = **a**, $\overrightarrow{OB}$ = **b** and $\overrightarrow{BC}$ = 2**a**. P and Q are the midpoints of $\overrightarrow{OB}$ and $\overrightarrow{AC}$. Express in terms of **a** and **b**.

a $\overrightarrow{OP}$ **b** $\overrightarrow{AQ}$ **c** $\overrightarrow{PQ}$ **d** How can you tell that $\overrightarrow{PQ}$ is parallel to $\overrightarrow{OA}$?

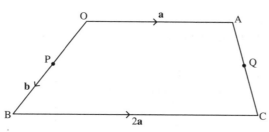

6 $\overrightarrow{OA}$, $\overrightarrow{OB}$ are the vectors **a** and **b**. C is the point on AB such that C is $\frac{3}{4}$ along AB.

a Express $\overrightarrow{OC}$ in terms of **a** and **b**.

b If D is the point that is $\frac{2}{3}$ along AC, write down the vector $\overrightarrow{OD}$.

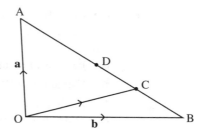

7 In the diagram, X is the point on AB such that AX = 4XB. Given that $\overrightarrow{OA}$ = 10**q** and $\overrightarrow{OB}$ = 5**p**, express in terms of **p** and/or **q**:

a $\overrightarrow{AB}$ **b** $\overrightarrow{AX}$ **c** $\overrightarrow{OX}$

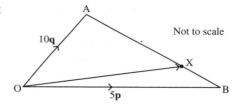

Not to scale

AU 8 ABCDEF is a regular hexagon with O as the centre.

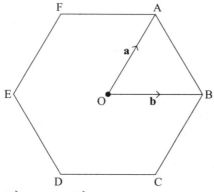

$\overrightarrow{OA}$ = **a** and $\overrightarrow{OB}$ = **b**

a Express each of the following vectors in terms of **a** and **b**.
Give your answers in their simplest form.

   i $\overrightarrow{AB}$ **ii** $\overrightarrow{AD}$ **iii** $\overrightarrow{EC}$ **iv** $\overrightarrow{FB}$

b Write down two facts about the lines EC and FB.

AU 9 A, B and C are three points with:
$$\overrightarrow{AB} = 6\mathbf{a} + 4\mathbf{b} \text{ and } \overrightarrow{AC} = 9\mathbf{a} + 6\mathbf{b}$$

a Write down a fact about the points A, B and C.
Give a reason for your answer.

b Write down the ratio of the lengths AB : BC in its simplest form.

13.2 Vectors in geometry

HOMEWORK 13B

A*

1 OACB is a rectangle. $\vec{OA} = \mathbf{a}$ and $\vec{OB} = \mathbf{b}$.
Q is the midpoint of BC and P divides BA in the
ratio 1 : 2. Find the vectors:

a $\vec{BP}$ **b** $\vec{OP}$ **c** $\vec{OQ}$

d Explain the relationship between O, P and Q.

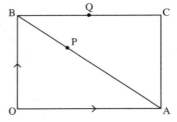

2 $\vec{OA} = \mathbf{a}$. $\vec{OB} = \mathbf{b}$. P is the point that divides OB in
the ratio 1 : 2. Q is the point that divides OA in the
ratio 2 : 1.

a Express in terms of $\mathbf{a}$ and $\mathbf{b}$:   **i** $\vec{AP}$ **ii** $\vec{BQ}$

b Explain why OR can be written as $\mathbf{a} + n\vec{AP}$.

c Explain why OR can be written as $\mathbf{b} + m\vec{BQ}$.

d Show that the expressions in parts **b** and **c** are
equal when $n = \frac{3}{7}$ and $m = \frac{6}{7}$.

e Hence find the vector $\vec{OR}$ in terms of $\mathbf{a}$ and $\mathbf{b}$.

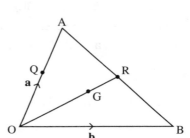

3 OAB is a triangle. $\vec{OA} = \mathbf{a}$. $\vec{OB} = \mathbf{b}$. R is the
midpoint of AB. Q is the midpoint of OA.
Find in terms of $\mathbf{a}$ and $\mathbf{b}$ the vectors:

a $\vec{OR}$ **b** $\vec{QB}$

c G is the point where OR and QB meet.
Explain why $\vec{OG}$ can be written both as $n\,\vec{OR}$
and $\frac{1}{2}\mathbf{a} + m(\vec{QB})$.

d You are given that $m + n = 1$.
Find values of m and n that satisfy the equations in **c**.

e Hence express $\vec{OG}$ in terms of $\mathbf{a}$ and $\mathbf{b}$.

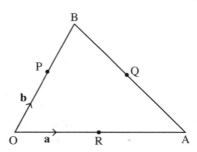

4 OAB is a triangle. P, Q and R are the midpoints
of OB, OA and AB. $\vec{OR} = \mathbf{a}$ and $\vec{OP} = \mathbf{b}$.

a Express in terms of $\mathbf{a}$ and $\mathbf{b}$ the vectors:
   i $\vec{RP}$ **ii** $\vec{AB}$

b What can you say about $\vec{RP}$ and $\vec{AB}$?

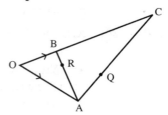

5 OAC is a triangle such that $\vec{OC} = 12\mathbf{q}$, $\vec{OB} = 3\mathbf{q}$ and $\vec{OA} = 3\mathbf{p}$.

a Find in terms of $\mathbf{p}$ and $\mathbf{q}$ the vectors:
   i $\vec{AB}$ **ii** $\vec{AC}$

b Given that $AQ = \frac{1}{3}AC$ express $\vec{OQ}$ in terms
of $\mathbf{p}$ and $\mathbf{q}$.

c Given that $\vec{OR} = \mathbf{p} + 2\mathbf{q}$ what can you say
about the points O, R and Q?

AU **6** OABC is a quadrilateral. $\vec{OA}$ = **a**, $\vec{OB}$ = **b**, $\vec{OC}$ = **c**.
M, N, Q and P are the midpoints of OA, OB, CB
and AC, respectively.

a Find in terms of **a**, **b** and **c** the vectors:
  i $\vec{BC}$ **ii** $\vec{NQ}$ **iii** $\vec{MP}$
b What type of quadrilateral is MNQP?
Explain your answer.

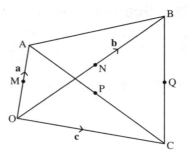

7 OACB and OBRS are parallelograms.
$\vec{OA}$ is **a**, $\vec{OB}$ is **b**, and $\vec{BR}$ is **r**. Find in terms of **a**, **b**
and **r** expressions in their simplest forms for:

a $\vec{OR}$
b $\vec{SB}$
c $\vec{OX}$, where X is the midpoint of AR,
  i.e. $\frac{1}{2}(\vec{AO} + \vec{OR})$

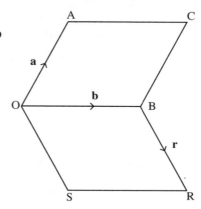

AU **8** On the diagram, $\vec{OA}$ = **a**, $\vec{OB}$ = **b** and $\vec{OC}$ = 3**b** − 2**a**.

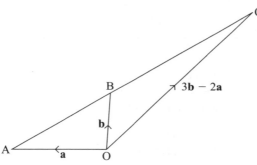

Prove that ABC is a straight line.

AU **9** OACB is a trapezium with $\vec{OA}$ = 3**a**,
$\vec{OB}$ = 4**b** and $\vec{BC}$ = 6**c**.

a Find these vectors in terms of **a** and **b**.
  i $\vec{OC}$ **ii** $\vec{AB}$
b Point M lies on AB with
  AM : MB = 1 : 2.
  Find $\vec{OM}$ in terms of **a** and **b**.
  Give your answer in its simplest form.
c Explain why OMC is a straight line.

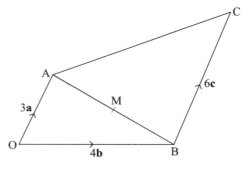

13.3 Geometric proof

HOMEWORK 13C

A*

PS 1 ABCD is a trapezium. The diagonals DB and AC meet at E.
Prove that triangles ADE and BCE are equal in area.

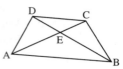

PS 2 ABCD is a rectangle. CEF is a triangle
congruent to triangle ACD. BCE is a straight
line. The line AC is extended to meet EF at P.
Prove that AP is perpendicular to EF.

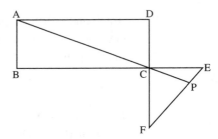

PS 3 An isosceles trapezium is cut along a diagonal and the pieces are put together as shown.

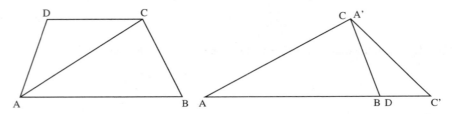

a Prove that ABC' is a straight line.
b Prove that the large triangle is isosceles.
c Explain why the triangle formed of the two pieces could never be equilateral.

PS 4 The midpoints of the edges of a square are
joined to a vertex to create a smaller square (shown
shaded). Explain why the shaded square has an area
one-fifth of the area of the larger square.

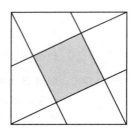

PS 5 ABC is a triangle. P is a point on BC such
that angle APC = angle BAC. The sides of ABC
are a, b and c. AP = p and PC = r.
Prove that: $r = \dfrac{b^2}{a}$

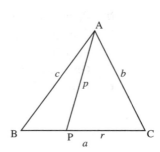

HINTS AND TIPS

Show that triangles ABC
and APC are similar.

PS 6 **a** Prove that the angles subtended by a chord at the circumference of a circle are equal.

b PQRS is a cyclic quadrilateral. PR and QS meet at T. Angles x, $2x$, $3x$ and $5x$ are marked on the diagram.

    i Find x.

    ii Show that the angles of the quadrilateral and angle STP form a number sequence.

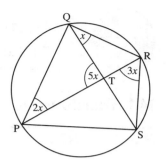

PS 7 ACB and ADB are right-angled triangles. The lengths are as marked.

a Use Pythagoras' theorem to show that $x^2 = r^2 + s^2$.

b Use Pythagoras' theorem on both triangles ACB and ADB to prove that: $xt = sy$

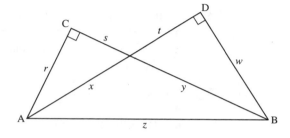

Problem-solving Activity

Vectors on a chess board

A Knight is on the white square near the bottom left-hand corner of a chess board.

The two possible moves it can make are shown by the vectors **a** and **b**.

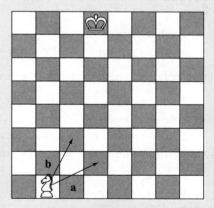

Using only combinations of these two types of move, how many different ways can the Knight reach the King at the top?

Algebra: Transformation of graphs

14.1 Transformations of the graph $y = f(x)$

HOMEWORK 14A

You may use a graphical calculator or a graph drawing program to do this exercise.

1 On the same axes sketch the graphs of:

   a $y = x^2$ **b** $y = 2x^2$ **c** $y = x^2 + 2$ **d** $y = (x + 2)^2$

   e   Describe the transformation(s) that take(s) the graph in part **a** to each of the graphs in parts **b** to **d**.

2 On the same axes sketch the graphs of:

   a $y = x^2$ **b** $y = 3x^2 + 2$ **c** $y = x^2 - 3$ **d** $y = \frac{1}{2}x^2 + 1$

   e   Describe the transformation(s) that take(s) the graph in part **a** to each of the graphs in parts **b** to **d**.

3 On the same axes sketch the graphs of:

   a $y = x^2$ **b** $y = (x + 4)^2$ **c** $y = -x^2$ **d** $y = 2 - x^2$

   e   Describe the transformation(s) that take(s) the graph in part **a** to each of the graphs in parts **b** to **d**.

4 On the same axes sketch the graphs of:

   a $y = \sin x$ **b** $y = 3\sin x$ **c** $y = \sin x + 3$ **d** $y = \sin (x + 30°)$

   e   Describe the transformation(s) that take(s) the graph in part **a** to each of the graphs in parts **b** to **d**.

5 On the same axes sketch the graphs of:

   a $y = \sin x$ **b** $y = -\sin x$ **c** $y = \sin \frac{x}{3}$ **d** $y = 3\sin \frac{x}{2}$

   e   Describe the transformation(s) that take(s) the graph in part a to each of the graphs in parts **b** to **d**.

6 On the same axes sketch the graphs of:

   a $y = \sin x$ **b** $y = 3\sin x$ **c** $y = \sin (x + 45°)$ **d** $y = 2\sin (x + 90°)$

   e   Describe the transformation(s) that take(s) the graph in part **a** to the graphs in parts **b** to **d**.

7 On the same axes sketch the graphs of:

   a $y = \cos x$ **b** $y = -\cos x$ **c** $y = \cos x + 4$ **d** $y = 2\cos x$

   e   Describe the transformation(s) that take(s) the graph in part **a** to each of the graphs in parts **b** to **d**.

8 On the same axes sketch the graphs of:

   a $y = \cos x$ **b** $y = 3\cos x$ **c** $y = \cos (x + 60°)$ **d** $y = 2\cos x + 3$

   e   Describe the transformation(s) that take(s) the graph in part **a** to each of the graphs in parts **b** to **d**.

9 Explain why the graphs of $y = \cos x$ and $y = \sin (x + 90°)$ are the same.

10 The table shows some values of the function $f(x) = (x - 2)^2 + 4$, where $-3 < x < 4$.

a Draw the graph of $y = f(x)$.

b On the same axes, draw the graph of:
$y = x^2$.

x	-3	-2	-1	0	1	2	3	4
$f(x)$	29	20	13	8	5	4	5	8

c Describe how the graph of $y = (x - 2)^2 + 4$ can be obtained from the graph $y = x^2$ by a transformation. State clearly what this transformation is.

PS 11 The graphs below are all transformations of $y = x^2$. Two points through which each graph passes are indicated. Use this information to work out the equation of each graph.

a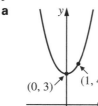

b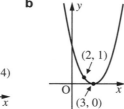

c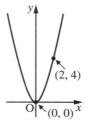

d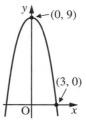

PS 12 The graphs below are all transformations of $y = \sin x$. Two points through which each graph passes are indicated. Use this information to work out the equation of each graph.

a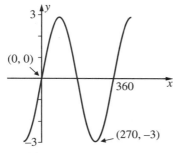

b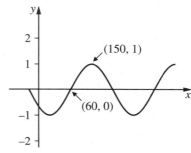

c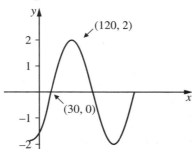

d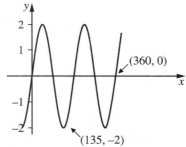

AU 13 Below are the graphs of: $y = -\sin x$ and $y = \cos x$

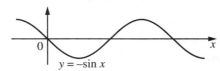 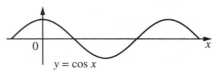

a Describe a series of transformations that would take the first graph to the second.

b Which of the following is equivalent to $y = -\sin x$?

i $y = \sin(x + 180°)$ **ii** $y = \cos(x + 90°)$ **iii** $y = 2\sin\dfrac{x}{2}$

A*

14 The graph of $y = f(x)$ has been drawn.
Sketch the graphs of:

a $y = f(x) - 2$ **b** $y = f(x - 2)$

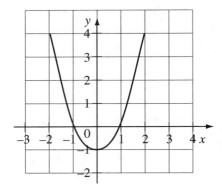

Problem-solving Activity

Transforming graphs

The sketch below shows the graphs of $y = x^2$ and $y = x^2 + 3x$

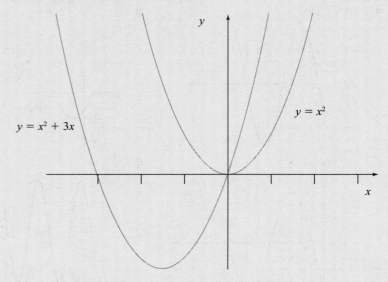

1 **a** Write down the coordinates of the minimum point of the equation:
$y = x^2 + 3x$

  b Describe how the graph of $y = x^2 + 3x$ can be transformed from the graph of:
$y = x^2$

2 Now draw graphs of $y = x^2 + 4x$, $y = x^2 - 2x$ and $y = x^2 - x$ on the same axes.

  a Describe anything that you notice about these graphs.

  b Describe how you could obtain the graph of $y = x^2 + ax$ by transforming the graph of $y = x^2$

William Collins' dream of knowledge for all began with the publication of his first book in 1819. A self-educated mill worker, he not only enriched millions of lives, but also founded a flourishing publishing house. Today, staying true to this spirit, Collins books are packed with inspiration, innovation and practical expertise. They place you at the centre of a world of possibility and give you exactly what you need to explore it.

Collins. Freedom to teach.

Published by Collins
An imprint of HarperCollins*Publishers*
77–85 Fulham Palace Road
Hammersmith
London
W6 8JB

Browse the complete Collins catalogue at
www.collinseducation.com

10 9 8 7 6 5 4 3 2 1

ISBN-13 978-0-00-734014-9

Brian Speed, Keith Gordon, Keith Evans, Trevor Senior and Chris Pearce assert their moral rights to be identified as the authors of this work

British Library Cataloguing in Publication Data
A Catalogue record for this publication is available from the British Library

Commissioned by Katie Sergeant
Project managed by Patricia Briggs
Edited by Brian Asbury
Answers checked by Steven Matchett and Joan Miller
Cover design by Angela English
Concept design by Nigel Jordan
Illustrations by Wearset Publishing Services
Typesetting by Wearset Publishing Services
Production by Arjen Jansen
Printed and bound by L.E.G.O. S.p.A. Italy

Important information about the Student Book CD-ROM
The accompanying CD-ROM is for home use only. You cannot copy or save the files to your hard drive and it will work only when placed in the CD-ROM drive.